Name_____

All About:

Kites

Kites are fun on a windy day. They fly up in the sky. Kites come in many colors. They look pretty as they fly.

 the kites: **1** - red
2 - yellow
3 - blue

| kite |
| sky |
| windy |

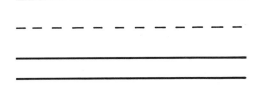

 Where do kites fly?   sky
table

• Draw and color a pretty kite.

All About:

Kittens

Do you like kittens?
Kittens are soft and cute.
They like to run and jump.
They play with . Kittens
like to drink milk, too.

tall   jump

_ _ _ _ _ _ _ _ _ _ _ _ _

 Kittens like to run and

 What do kittens play with?

sun   yarn

 Kittens like to drink ☐ call.
☐ milk.

 kitten - yellow
yarn - red

• Draw and color three kittens.

Name_____

All About:

Puppies

Puppies are full of love.
They like to be your friends.
Some puppies are brown.
Some puppies are black.
Have you ever seen a puppy
with spots?

 Puppies like to be your

friends.
farm.

_____

- - - - - - - - - - - - - -

| puppies |
| puppy |

_____

- - - - - - - - - - - - - -

_____

 Some puppies are

brown   blue

_____

- - - - - - - - - - - - - - .

Some puppies are _____ .

purple   black

- - - - - - - - - - - - - - .

Some puppies are _____ .

• Draw and color a puppy you would like to have.

All About:

Name_____

A Picnic

A picnic is fun on a sunny day. You can eat hot dogs, chips and lots of . Then, you can run and play games.

What day is good for a picnic?

green   games

_____

It is fun to run and play _____.

a red hot dog in the bun.

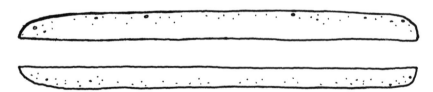

five black seeds in the watermelon.

• Draw and color a picture of **yourself** at a picnic.

All About:

Name_____

Letters

Letters, letters, all around,
They go from **A** to **Z**.
Letters help you write your name.
They make each word you see.

Letters go from _____ to _____ .

letters	colors

Each word is made of _____ .

Letters help you write your
cake.
name.

Go from **A** to **Z** in the picture.

• Write your **A B C**'s.

All About:

Clouds

Name_____

Clouds look pretty in the sky. They can be white and puffy. Clouds are made of water. That is where rain comes from. Rain comes from clouds.

Clouds look pretty in the _____ table. sky.

white	five	puffy

Clouds can be _____ and _____ .

☐ I am made of water.
☐ I am a tree.
☐ I give you rain.

• Draw and color four clouds in a blue sky.

All About:

Ice Cream

Ice cream is fun to eat on a hot day. You can have ice cream in a cone or dish. It comes in many yummy flavors. Which do you like best?

hat   hot

Ice cream is fun on a _____ day.

Draw two 's of ice cream in the cone.
Draw three 's of ice cream in the dish.

the ice cream picture: **1**-brown, **2**-pink, **3**-yellow

• Draw a cone filled with ice cream you like the best.

All About:

Pets

It is fun to have a pet. Dogs and cats are good pets. Birds and rabbits can be pets, too. Pets are good friends. They need care and love every day.

friends   fast
_____
- - - - - - - - - - - -
Pets are good _____ .

Pets need care and   long.
                      love.

| dog | rabbit | cat | bird |

_____   _____
- - - - - - - -   - - - - - - - -
_____   _____

_____   _____
- - - - - - - -   - - - - - - - -
_____   _____

• Draw and color a picture of your pet.

All About:

Stars

Do you see the stars at night? They shine in the sky. The stars look very small. That is because they are so far away.

You can see the stars at
train.
night.

The stars _____ shine   saw _____ in the sky.

Why do the stars look so small?

☐ They are far away.
☐ They are happy.

the stars yellow.

• Draw and color five yellow stars.

All About:

The Sun

You can see the sun in the daytime. It looks round and yellow. The sun is a big star. It gives us light. It helps keep us warm.

When can you see the sun?

night

day

sit   star

_ _ _ _ _ _ _ _

The sun is a big _____ .

light   pet

_ _ _ _ _ _ _ _

I give you _____ .

run   warm

_ _ _ _ _ _ _ _

I keep you _____ .

a yellow sun in the picture.

• Draw and color what you like to do on a sunny day.

All About:

A Farm

A farm is a home for some animals. Horses, cows and pigs live on a farm. Sheep and chickens are farm animals, too. Many farm animals live in a big barn.

 Which animals live on a farm?

ride   farm
_____

- - - - - - - - - - - - - -

A _____ is a home for some animals.

Many farm animals live in a big

- Draw and color two farm animals.

barn.

All About:

A Birthday

Every year you have a birthday. You are one year older. It is fun to have a birthday party and a cake. The  on the cake tell how old you are.

Every year you have a

birthday.
barn.

It is fun to have a birthday _____ .

party   puppy

What can tell how old you are?

candles   balloon

 blue on the cake to tell how old you are.

• Draw and color a big birthday cake just for you.

Name_____

All About:

Summer Camp

There is much to do at summer camp. You can swim and hike. You can ride in a  . At night, you can sit around the fire and sing.

house   camp
_____
- - - - - - - - - - - - - - - -

 There is much to do at summer _____.

| sing   hike   swim |

 <u>canoe</u>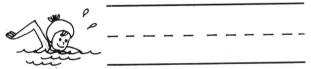

_____

 the 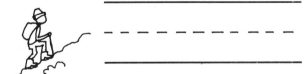 red.

• Draw a picture of **yourself** at summer camp.

All About:

Shapes

There are shapes all around us. A box can be ☐.

A party hat can be like a △.
A ball is a ○. A kite can be like a ◇. What is like a ▭ ?

star   shapes

There are _____ all around us.

_____ circle   ○

square   ☐

triangle   △

diamond   ◇

rectangle   ▭

• Draw and color a ○, ☐, △, ◇ and ▭ .

Name_____

All About:

School

Going to school helps you learn many things. You learn to read and write and spell. Your teacher helps you learn math, too. You will make new friends at school.

 You learn new things at step. school.

| read |
| spell |
| math |
| write |

$+\dfrac{2}{3}{5}$

_____

- - - - - - - - - - -

_____

- - - - - - - - - - -

_____

- - - - - - - - - - -

_____

- - - - - - - - - - -

 your name on the ▨ .

- Draw and color a picture of **your** school.

All About:

Cowboys

A cowboy lives on a ranch. He takes care of cattle. He rides horses. A cowboy wears a big hat and tall boots. He works very hard.

 A cowboy lives on a

ranch.
ride.

A cowboy takes care of _____.

bugs   cattle

☐ I ride a horse.
☐ I wear a big hat.
☐ I live in the city.
☐ I wear tall boots.

the horse brown.

• Draw and color a picture of a cowboy.

All About:

Friends

A friend is someone you like very much. Friends play together. Friends help each other, too. It is nice to have many friends.

 _____friend_____from_____

A _____ is someone you like.

Yes or **No**

Friends play together.   Yes   No

Friends are cars.   Yes   No

Friends help each other.   Yes   No

Which are friends?

• Draw and color a picture of you and your friends.

All About:

Feelings

People can have many feelings. They can be happy. They can be sad. Sometimes people can feel angry. Everyone has feelings.

People can have many _____ five. feelings.

| happy |
| angry |
| sad |

_____
- - - - - - - - - -
_____
- - - - - - - - - -
_____
- - - - - - - - - -
_____

Make the faces look:

happy   sad   angry

• Draw and color a picture of how you feel.

All About:

Babies

Everyone begins as a baby. A baby needs love and care. Sometimes babies cry when they are hungry. Babies like to drink lots of milk.

cook   baby

_____

_ _ _ _ _ _ _ _ _ _ _ _

 Everyone begins as a _____ .

Yes or **No**

A baby needs love and care.	Yes	No
A baby is very tall.	Yes	No
Sometimes babies cry.	Yes	No
Babies like to drink milk.	Yes	No

b - red
a - yellow
b - blue
y - green

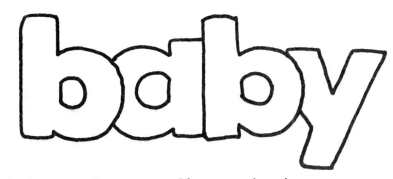

• Draw and color a picture of **yourself** as a baby.

Name_____

All About:

Names

Everyone has a name. Pets have names, too. Most people have a first name and a last name. Some people have a middle name. Do you?

That is short for Muffin.

Muff

call   name

_____

– – – – – – – – – – – –

✏ Everyone has a _____ .

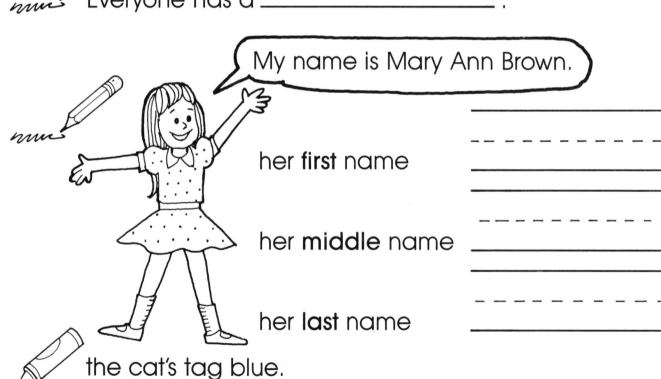

My name is Mary Ann Brown.

✏

_____

– – – – – – – – – – – –

her **first** name   _____

– – – – – – – – – – – –

her **middle** name   _____

– – – – – – – – – – – –

her **last** name   _____

the cat's tag blue.

• Write **your** whole name.

All About:

Shopping

People go shopping for many things. You can shop for food. You can shop for clothes. It is lots of fun to shop for new toys.

shopping   bus
_____
- - - - - - - - - - - - - - -

People go _____ for many things.

What can you shop for?

☐ You can shop for food.

☐ You can shop for clothes.

☐ You can shop for rain.

☐ You can shop for toys.

food - green   **clothes** - red   **toys** - yellow

• Draw and color what you would like to shop for.

All About:

Sizes

Name_____

🐴 's are big.
🐱 's are small.
People are short.
People are tall.
An 🐘 looks huge
To a little 🐝.

How many sizes can **you** see?

elephant	kittens	people

huge small	small big	little tall

bee	people	horses

little big	short tall	little big

the big picture: **big things** - red
little things - blue

• Draw and color a big thing and a small thing.

22

All About:

A Bus

A bus can take you many places. Some kids ride to school on a bus. People can ride to work on a bus. A bus can even take you to another city.

 Where can you go in a bus?

school
work
kite

_____

- - - - - - - -

_____

_____

- - - - - - - -

_____

A bus can even take you to another   dress.
city.

the bus yellow.

- Draw a bus with **yourself** as the driver!

All About:

Trucks

Trucks can carry lots of things. They can take food to the store. They can help you move to a new house. Trucks work very hard.

I am a truck.
trip.

What can trucks do?

☐ Trucks can take food to the store.

☐ Trucks can help you move.

☐ Trucks are people.

☐ Trucks can carry lots of things.

the truck green.

• Draw and color a big, red truck.

24

All About:

Trains

Have you ever been on a train? A train rides on tracks. The engine pulls the train. Many trains have a red at the end.

door   train

_____

A _____ rides on tracks.

 caboose

 _____

 _____

tracks

engine

1-blue   **2**-yellow   **3**-orange   **4**-green   **5**-red

• Draw and color a train.

All About:

Cars

Many people drive cars. A car helps you go places. You can ride in a car to places in your city. It is fun to go on a long car trip, too.

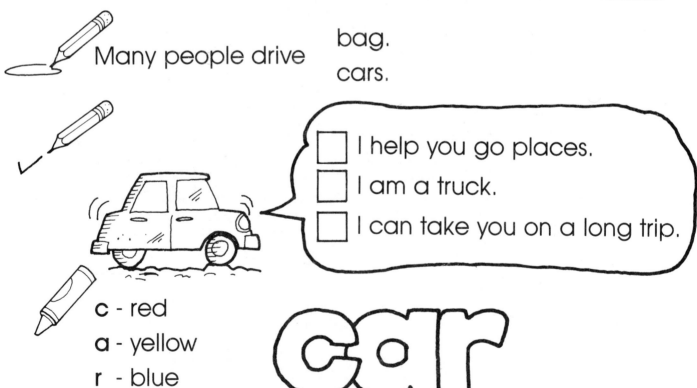

Many people drive ___

bag.
cars.

☐ I help you go places.

☐ I am a truck.

☐ I can take you on a long trip.

c - red
a - yellow
r - blue

car

• Draw and color two green cars.

All About:

Airplanes

It is fun to fly in an airplane. Airplanes fly high in the sky. You can look out the window and see the clouds. You can look down and see a city.

Airplanes fly high in the   hall.
                              sky.

What can you see from an airplane?

| clouds |
| talk |
| city |

_____
- - - - - - - - - - - -
_____
_____
- - - - - - - - - - - -
_____

two clouds in the picture.

• Draw and color a blue airplane.

All About:

Boats

There are many kinds of boats. Some boats have sails. A sailboat moves with the wind's help. Some boats have motors. They can go very fast.

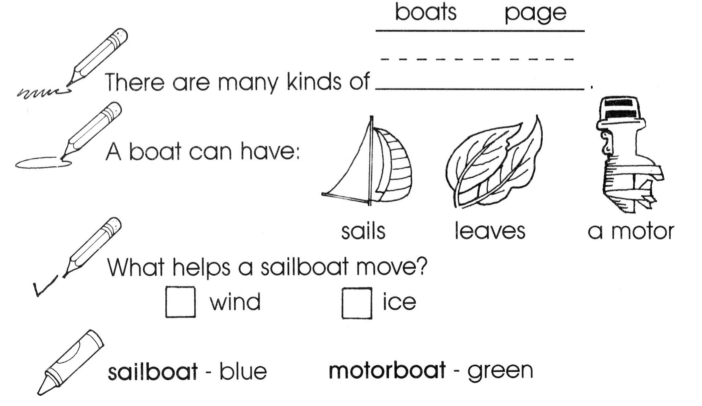

boats   page
_____

- - - - - - - - - - -

There are many kinds of _____.

A boat can have:

sails   leaves   a motor

What helps a sailboat move?

☐ wind   ☐ ice

sailboat - blue   **motorboat** - green

• Draw and color a boat with **you** in it.

All About:

Clowns

Clowns are funny to watch. They like to make you laugh. They wear funny clothes. They do lots of tricks. Clowns like to give balloons and candy to kids.

laugh   cry

_____

- - - - - - - - - - - -

Clowns like to make you _____.

Yes or No

Clowns wear funny clothes.	Yes	No
Clowns do lots of tricks.	Yes	No
Clowns fly in the sky.	Yes	No
Clowns give balloons to kids.	Yes	No

the clown.

• Draw and color a picture of **yourself** as a clown.

Name_____

All About:

Days

There are seven days in a week. Saturday and Sunday are the weekend days. You go to school the other five days. Which day do you like best?

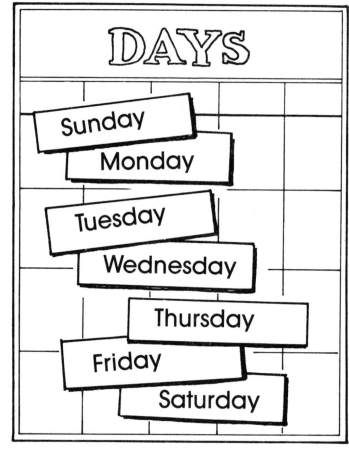

DAYS

Sunday
Monday
Tuesday
Wednesday
Thursday
Friday
Saturday

How many days are in a week?

  six   seven   ten

Which two days make a weekend?

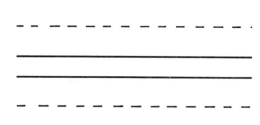

| Saturday |
| Thursday |
| Sunday |

_ _ _ _ _ _ _ _ _ _ _ _ _

_ _ _ _ _ _ _ _ _ _ _ _ _

  the five days you go to school.

• Draw and color what you do on a weekend.

Name_____

All About:

Trees

There are many kinds of trees. Some trees grow fruit. Some trees have flowers on them. Trees can be very tall. They need sun and water to grow.

 There are many kinds of

fast.

trees.

What can grow on trees?

What do trees need to grow?

- [ ] sun
- [ ] sleep
- [ ] water

five red apples on the tree.

• Draw and color a green tree.

Name_____

All About:

Fruit

Do you like to eat fruit? Fruit is good for you. , apples and  are kinds of fruit. Oranges and are fruit, too. Which fruit do you like the best?

fall   fruit
_____
- - - - - - - - - - -
There are many kinds of _____ .

Which foods are fruit?

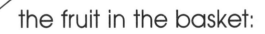

banana   grapes   apple

orange   steak   pear

the fruit in the basket:

1 - red   **2** - green   **3** - purple

4 - orange   **5** - yellow

• Draw and color the fruit **you** like best.

All About:

Basketball

Some basketball players are very tall. They run and bounce the ball. They throw the ball into the net. They want to win the game.

Some basketball players are very

small.
tall.

throw
bounce

_____

- - - - - - - - -

_____

- - - - - - - - -

_____

the basketball brown.

• Draw and color a basketball player.

All About:

Swimming

Swimming is fun on a hot day. You can swim in a pool. You can go to the beach and swim in the ocean. The water helps you feel cool.

swim   way

_____

- - - - - - - - - - - -

It is fun to _____ on a hot day.

Where can you swim?

The water helps you feel ☐ hot.
☐ cool.

• Draw and color a picture of where you like to swim.

All About:

Baseball

A baseball game is fun to watch. You can eat a hot dog and . You can yell and cheer. You may see your team hit a home run!

___pet___ ___game___
_____

A baseball _____ is fun to watch.

You can eat: hot dog   pepper   popcorn

| yell | sleep | cheer |

_____   _____

You can _____ and _____.

a red **X** on the man with the ball.

• Draw and color a baseball and bat.

Name_____

All About:

Soccer

Do you know how to play soccer? You run and kick the ball. You can hit the ball with your head. But, you cannot touch the ball with your hands!

_____ kick   sit _____

- - - - - - - - - -

1. Run and _____ the ball.

_____ mat   head _____

- - - - - - - - - -

2. You can hit the ball with your _____.

_____ hands   dish _____

- - - - - - - - - -

3. You cannot touch the ball with your _____.

1 - red

2 - blue

• Draw and color a green and orange soccer ball.

Name_____

All About:

Spring

It is warm in the spring.
Flowers begin to bloom.
Trees have new .
Birds make their nests and
lay eggs. Do you like to fly
a kite in the spring?

warm   last

It is _____ in the spring.

What can you see in the spring?

What do birds do in the spring?

- [ ] Birds make nests.
- [ ] They lay eggs.
- [ ] They wash dishes.

• Draw and color a nest with four eggs in it.

Name_____

All About:

Autumn

The air gets cool in the autumn. Kids go back to school. Animals store food for the winter. Leaves turn red, yellow and orange. It is a pretty time of the year.

time   cool
_____

- - - - - - - - - -

The air gets _____ in the autumn.

What happens in the autumn?

☐ Kids go back to school.

☐ Animals store food.

☐ The air is very hot.

red   yellow   orange

- Draw and color an autumn tree.

All About:

Winter

Winter can be cold and snowy. Animals stay near each other to keep warm. People wear coats, hats and . Kids can make a snowman. It is fun to play in the snow.

Winter can be:
- ☐ cold
- ☐ snowy
- ☐ purple

like   warm

We try to stay _____.

What do people wear in the winter?

gloves   hat   pan   coat

a black 🎩 on the ⛄.

• Draw and color a snowman.

All About:

Birds

Do you like to see birds fly? Some birds have pretty . Most birds like to live in trees. They eat seeds and worms and bugs.

Yes or **No**

Some birds have pretty feathers.	Yes	No
Most birds live in trees.	Yes	No
Birds live in tents.	Yes	No

What do birds like to eat?

seeds	worms	butter	bugs

_____ _____ _____

- - - - - - - - - - - - - - - - - - - - - - - - - - -

_____ _____ _____

• Draw and color two birds.

All About:

Tigers

Tigers live in the jungle. They like to hunt for food at night. Tigers can climb trees. They can run fast. Tigers are very strong animals.

Tigers live in the   jungle.
table.

store   night

Tigers like to hunt for food at _____.

What can tigers do?

climb trees   cook   run fast

the tiger: **body** - orange   **stripes** - black

• Draw and color a tiger in a jungle.

All About:

Snakes

There are many kinds of snakes. Some snakes are very long. Some snakes are small. Snakes do not have legs. They crawl on the ground. They can move quickly.

Yes or **No**

Snakes do not have legs.	Yes	No
Snakes crawl on the ground.	Yes	No
Snakes cannot move.	Yes	No

| long |
| bird |
| small |

_____

- - - - - - - - - - - -

_____

- - - - - - - - - - - -

_____

the snakes green.

• Draw and color a long, brown snake.

All About:

Bats

Bats like to fly at night. They sleep in the daytime. A bat sleeps by hanging upside down. Most bats live in trees and caves. Have you ever seen a bat?

night   noon
_____
- - - - - - - - - -

Bats like to fly at _____.

Bats sleep in the   room.
                     daytime.

How do bats sleep?

Most bats live in: ☐ trees
                    ☐ caves
                    ☐ floor

the bats black.

• Draw and color a cave with sleeping bats in it.

Name_____

All About:

Seals

Seals swim in the ocean. They come out on the land to rest. Seals like to eat fish. Some seals can learn to do tricks. Have you ever seen a seal do a trick?

Yes or **No**

Seals swim in the ocean.	Yes	No
Seals rest on the land.	Yes	No
Seals can walk many miles.	Yes	No
Some seals can learn tricks.	Yes	No

✓ What do seals like to eat?
☐ beans   ☐ fish

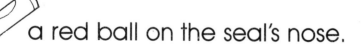

a red ball on the seal's nose.

• Draw and color a seal in the ocean.

All About:

Elephants

An elephant is a very large animal. Its long nose is called a trunk. The trunk takes food and water to the elephant's mouth. Would you like to ride on an elephant?

tiny   large
_____

- - - - - - - - - - - -

An elephant is a very _____ animal.

An elephant's nose is called a   trunk.
                                  bag.

What can a trunk put in an elephant's mouth?
☐ food   ☐ boat   ☐ water

Make a trunk on the elephant.

• Draw and color a gray elephant.

All About:

Giraffes

Name_____

A giraffe is a very tall animal. It has a long, long neck. Giraffes can eat leaves from tall trees. They have long, thin legs. A giraffe has spots on its body. Have you ever seen a giraffe?

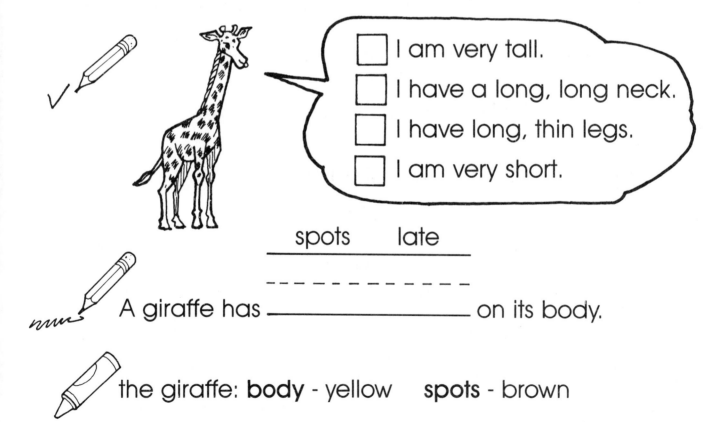

☐ I am very tall.

☐ I have a long, long neck.

☐ I have long, thin legs.

☐ I am very short.

spots   late

_____

A giraffe has _____ on its body.

the giraffe: **body** - yellow   **spots** - brown

• Draw and color a baby giraffe.

All About:

Spiders

There are many kinds of spiders. Spiders have eight legs. They like to eat insects. Many spiders spin a web. The web is the spider's home. Have you ever seen a spider's web?

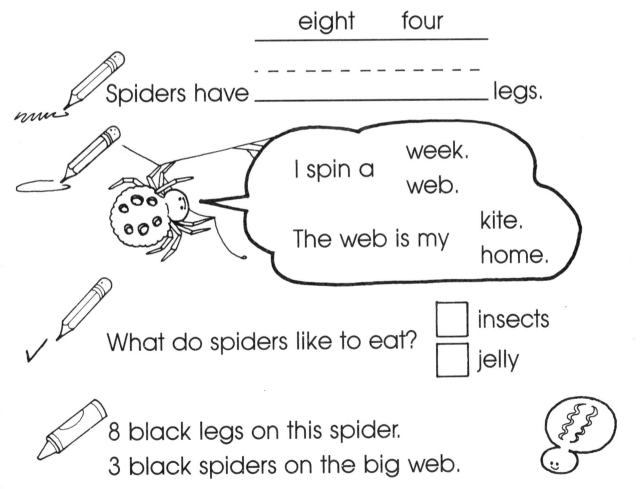

eight   four

_____

- - - - - - - - - - - -

Spiders have _____ legs.

I spin a   week.
           web.

The web is my   kite.
                home.

What do spiders like to eat?   ☐ insects
                                ☐ jelly

8 black legs on this spider.

3 black spiders on the big web.

• Draw and color a spider and its web.

All About:

Zebras

A zebra has a white body with black stripes. It looks much like a horse. Zebras like to eat grass. They can run very fast. Have you ever seen a zebra at the zoo?

black   red
_____

A zebra has _____ stripes on its body.

A zebra looks much like a   horse.
house.

What do zebras eat? ☐ gate
                     ☐ grass

black stripes on the zebra.

• Draw and color a black and white zebra.

All About:

Turtles

A turtle has a shell on its back. The shell is the turtle's home. A turtle can pull its head and legs into the shell. Some turtles live in the water. Some turtles live on the land. Have you ever seen a turtle?

Yes or **No**

A turtle has a shell on its back.	Yes	No
The shell is the turtle's home.	Yes	No
A turtle is very tall.	Yes	No

Where can turtles live?

land	star	water

_____   _____

- - - - - - - - - - -   - - - - - - - - - - -

_____   _____

the turtles green.

• Draw and color two turtles.

49

All About:

Dinosaurs

Dinosaurs lived long, long ago. They were very big. Some dinosaurs ate meat. Other dinosaurs ate plants. Most dinosaurs lived on the land. But some lived in the water. Some pterodactyl's could fly!

When did dinosaurs live?   long ago
                              today

What did they eat?

meat
box
plants

_____
- - - - - - - - -
_____
_____
- - - - - - - - -

Where did dinosaurs live?

the big dinosaur

• Draw and color a big dinosaur.

Learn About: Colors

Making Colors

Did you know that all colors come from red, yellow or blue? They're the primary colors. Red and blue make purple. Blue and yellow make green. Yellow and red make orange. It is fun to mix paint to make new colors.

Circle.

Which three colors do you need to make all colors?

red   green   yellow   blue   pink

Write.

Red, yellow and blue are _____ colors.

orange   primary

Match.

Red and blue make   orange.

Blue and yellow make   purple.

Yellow and red make   green.

Color the picture: **1** - red   **2** - yellow   **3** - blue

                  4 - orange **5** - purple **6** - green

• Draw and color a picture using the **primary** colors.

Learn About:

The Five Senses

Your body has five senses. You can hear, see, touch, smell and taste with parts of your body.
You **see** with your eyes.
You **hear** with your ears.
You **smell** with your nose.
You **taste** with your tongue.
You **touch** with your hands.
Your five senses help you enjoy the world around you.

s	s	e	e	t
m	p	h	j	o
e	v	e	y	u
l	m	a	h	c
l	r	r	b	h
t	a	s	t	e

Circle.

How many senses do you have?   10   5   7

see	smell	touch
hear	taste	

Write.

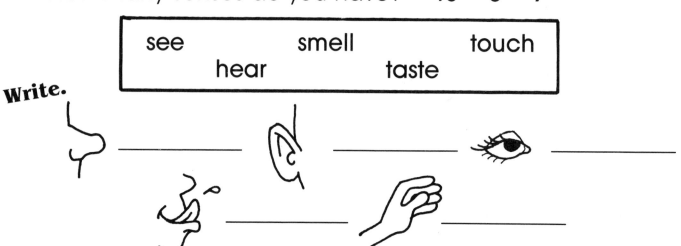

Circle the five senses in the puzzle above.

• Draw and color your favorite things to **hear** and **taste**.

Learn About:

Months

There are twelve months in a year. The first month is January. The last month is December. Some months have 31 days. Some months have 30 days. February is the shortest month with 28 days. Can you name the months of the year?

☐ April
☐ October
☐ December
☐ July
☐ March
[1] January
☐ May
☐ September
☐ June
☐ February
☐ August
☐ November

Check.
How many months are in a year?

☐ five
☐ nine
☐ twelve

Write.

_____   _____
first month   last month

Circle.

Yes or No

Some months have 30 days.	Yes	No
Some months have 31 days.	Yes	No
February is the longest month.	Yes	No
February has 28 days.	Yes	No

Write **1-12** in the ☐'s to put the months in order.

• Write the names of the twelve months in the correct order.

Learn About:

Seasons

Every year has four seasons. Winter can be cold and snowy. In spring, flowers bloom and trees grow new leaves. Summer can be very hot. It is a good time for swimming and picnics. In autumn, the air gets cooler. Leaves fall from trees. Animals store food for the cold weather to come.

Circle.

Every year has   seven   seasons.
                  four

Write.

winter   spring   summer   autumn

_____ A good time to build a snowman

_____ A good time to rake leaves

_____ A good time to go to the beach

_____ A good time to plant a garden

Write the correct season on each line in the picture.

Underline.

Put a line under the name of each season in the story.

• Draw and color a picture of your favorite season.

Learn About:

Weather

Weather is what it is like outside. Weather is always changing. There are many kinds of weather: hot, cold, rainy, snowy, foggy and stormy. Weather can be very helpful. Plants need sun and rain to live. Many animals need special weather, too. Polar bears like cold weather. Camels like hot weather. Which do you like best?

Circle.

Yes or No

Weather is what it is like outside.	Yes	No
Weather is always the same.	Yes	No
Plants need sun and rain.	Yes	No

hot	cold	rainy	snowy	foggy	stormy

Write.

_____   _____   _____

_____   _____   _____

Color.

cold weather animal - white

hot weather animal - brown

• Draw and color a picture of your favorite weather.

Reading Comprehension IF8707   55   © 1990 Instructional Fair, Inc.

Learn About:

Money

Money has been used for many years to pay for things. Before people had money, they would trade one thing for another. Most people are paid money for their jobs. There are two kinds of money: paper money and coins. Can you count money?

Check.
Money is used to ☐ start a car.
☐ pay for things.

Underline.
What did people do before they had money?
People would trade one thing for another.
People would sing songs.

Circle.
Most people are paid money / salt for their jobs.

Match.
paper money
coins

Color.
paper money - green   **coins** - gray

• Draw a picture of people trading things before they had money.

Learn About:

Time

There are many ways we measure time. A year is made of 365 days. A week has seven days. A day has 24 hours. An hour is made of 60 minutes. A minute is made of 60 seconds. A second goes very quickly. Can you blink your eyes in one second?

Name_____

| day | year | minute | week | hour |

Write.

1 ↓ 365 days make a y __ __ __.

2 → Seven days make a w __ __ __.

3 → 24 hours make a d __ __.

4 → 60 minutes make an h __ __ __.

5 ↓ 60 seconds make a m __ __ __ __ __.

Write the answers in the puzzle above.

Check.

The words in the puzzle tell about ☐ money. ☐ time.

• Write a list of what you can do in **two** minutes.

Learn About:

Special Clothes

Many people need special clothes for their jobs. Uniforms are special clothes. Nurses, ball players and police officers wear uniforms. Costumes are special clothes, too. Clowns, actors and dancers wear costumes. Can you think of other kinds of special clothes?

Circle.

Many people need special clothes for their box. jobs.

| uniform | costume |

Write.

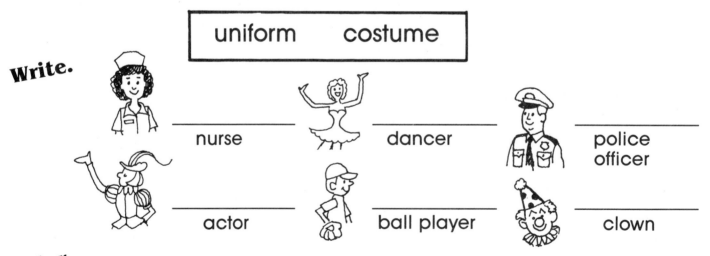

_____ nurse   _____ dancer   _____ police officer

_____ actor   _____ ball player   _____ clown

Color. uniforms - blue   costumes - green

• Draw and color another uniform and costume.

Learn About:

A Hobby

A hobby is something special that a person enjoys doing. Some people collect things as a hobby. They may collect stamps, coins or even comic books! Some people build things as a hobby. They may build furniture or model airplanes. Other hobbies are reading, sports and gardening. Do you have a hobby?

Name_____

Underline.
A hobby is   something you need to build houses.
something special that a person likes to do.

Write.
Some people _____ things as a hobby.
cover   collect

Circle.
What do some people collect?
stamps   ketchup   coins   comic books

Circle.
Some people   blue   things as a hobby.
build

Check.
They may build   ☐ clouds.
☐ furniture.
☐ model airplanes.

• Write about **your** hobby.

Learn About:

Earth

Earth is a planet. It is the planet where we live. Earth has land and water. It gets light and heat from the sun. Earth has one moon. Many people think there is life on other planets. Earth is the only planet that we know has life. Do **you** think there is life on other planets?

Unscramble.

Earth is the _____ where we live.

l e t p n a
2 5 6 1 4 3

Check.

☐ I have land and water.
☐ I get light and heat from the sun.
☐ I have five moons.
☐ I have one moon.
☐ I am a planet.

Circle.

Earth is the only planet that we know has
stars.
life.

Color.

Draw one yellow moon in the picture.

• Draw and color a picture of Earth.

Learn About:

The Moon

Do you ever look at the moon at night? The moon travels around the Earth. It gets its light from the sun. Men have gone to the moon in spaceships. They have walked on the moon. They even came back with moon rocks to study. Would you like to walk on the moon?

Circle.
The moon travels around the room.
Earth.

Write.
The moon gets its light from the _____.
Earth   sun

Check.
How did men go to the moon? ☐ spaceships
☐ automobiles

Circle.
Yes or No

Men have walked on the moon.   **Yes**   **No**

Circle.
What did men bring back from the moon?   stars
rocks

Color.
Draw a red spaceship on the moon.

• Draw what you would do if you went to the moon.

Learn About:

A Falling Star

Have you ever seen a falling star? Falling stars are not really stars. They are small pieces of rock. As falling stars fall, they get hot and burn. They look big because they give off so much light. That is why they are so bright in the night sky. Did you know that meteor is another name for a falling star?

Name_____

Circle.

Yes or No

A falling star is really a star.	Yes	No
Falling stars are pieces of rock.	Yes	No
Falling stars burn as they fall.	Yes	No

Check.

Why does a falling star give off light?

☐ It gets hot and burns.

☐ It has a light bulb in it.

Unscramble.

Another name for a falling star is _____.

e r m o t e
2 6 1 5 3 4

Color.

Draw two yellow falling stars in the picture.

• Write a poem about a falling star.

Learn About:

Deserts

A desert is very dry land that gets little rain. The air is very hot in the daytime. At night, the desert becomes very cool. Some deserts are made of sand. The wind blows the sand into little hills called sand dunes. Only a few plants and animals can live in the dry desert. Can you name a desert animal?

Circle.

Yes or No

A desert is very dry land.	Yes	No
A desert has a lot of rain.	Yes	No
A desert is hot in the daytime.	Yes	No
A desert is cool at night.	Yes	No

Write.

Some deserts are made of _____.

sticks   sand

Circle.

Which are sand dunes?

Check.

Only a few plants and animals can live in the ☐ dirt.
☐ desert.

Color.

Draw a brown camel in the desert.

• Write a list of what you would need to travel in a desert.

Learn About:

Oceans

Have you ever seen an ocean? An ocean is a very large body of water. Our Earth has four oceans. They have special names: Atlantic Ocean, Pacific Ocean, Indian Ocean and Arctic Ocean. The Pacific Ocean is the largest ocean. It is two times larger than the Atlantic Ocean.

Check.
What is an ocean?
☐ A large farm
☐ A large body of water

Circle.
How many oceans does the Earth have?
      seven   four   three

Write.
What are the names of the oceans? (Look at story.)

1 ↓ A _ _ _ _ _ _ _ _ Ocean

2 → A _ _ _ _ _ Ocean   3 → P _ _ _ _ _ _ Ocean

4 ↓ I _ _ _ _ _ Ocean

Write the names in the puzzle above.

Circle.
Which ocean is the largest?   Atlantic   Pacific

• Draw a picture of what you would find deep in an ocean.

Learn About:

Mountains

Mountains can be found in many parts of the world. Mountains are much taller than hills. A group of mountains together is called a mountain chain. A mountain's highest point is called a summit. The highest mountain in the world is Mount Everest. Mount Everest is in Asia.

Circle.

Yes or No

Mountains are much taller than hills.   Yes   No

A or B

(A) summit   (B) mountain chain

◯ A group of mountains together

◯ The highest point on a mountain

Unscramble.

The highest mountain in the world is Mount _____.

                                                    v r E e s e t
                                                    2 4 1 3 6 5 7

Mount Everest is in _____.

                    i A s a
                    3 1 2 4

Color.

Draw a red ⚑ flag on the summit of the tallest mountain.

• Draw a mountain chain with five mountains.

Learn About:

Exercise

Name_____

Do you like to exercise? Exercise is good for you. Walking and running are good ways to exercise. So are swimming and biking. Some people like to do push-ups, sit-ups and jumping jacks. Exercise can help you feel good. It can make your body stronger, too. What is your favorite kind of exercise?

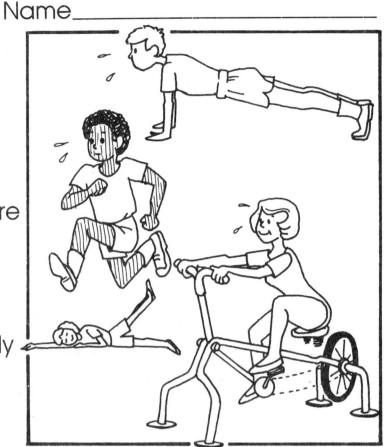

Unscramble.

_____ is good for you.

s r E c x i e e
7 4 1 5 2 6 3 8

Write.

| walking |
| swimming |
| biking |
| running |

_____

_____

_____

_____

Check.

What do some people do for exercise?

☐ push-ups ☐ sleep ☐ jumping jacks ☐ sit-ups

Circle.

Yes or No

Exercise can help you feel good.   Yes   No

Exercise is very easy.   Yes   No

Exercise can make your body stronger.   Yes   No

• Draw a picture of **you** exercising.

Name_____

Learn About:

Hiking

Have you ever gone hiking in the woods? Many people go on long hiking trips. They like to be outdoors. Hikers wear backpacks to carry what they need. They carry food and water. Most hikers use a compass to help them find their way. A compass tells which way they are going.

Underline.

Who would enjoy hiking?

People who don't like the outdoors.

People who enjoy being outdoors.

Write.

Hikers wear _____ to carry what they need.
umbrellas   backpacks

Write.

What could you find in a hiker's backpack?

water   compass

bike   food

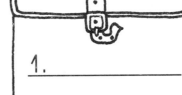

1. _____

2. _____

3. _____

Color.

the hikers' backpacks - brown   the hikers' compasses - red

• Draw a picture of **you** hiking in the woods.

Learn About:

Skateboarding

Many kids like to ride skateboards. Skateboards are short boards on wheels. Some cities have special places to ride skateboards. They are called skateboard parks. The parks have rules to keep kids safe. Kids must wear helmets on their heads. They must also wear kneepads and gloves.

Circle.

Yes or No

Many kids like to ride skateboards.	Yes	No
Skateboards are used to build houses.	Yes	No
Skateboards are short boards on wheels.	Yes	No
Some cities have skateboard parks.	Yes	No

Write.

Skateboard parks have _____ to keep kids safe.

jobs   rules

gloves

helmets

kneepads

RULES

1. Kids must wear _____.

2. Kids must wear _____ and _____

Color.

skateboards - red   helmets - blue

• Draw and color a green skateboard.

Name_____

Learn About:

Frisbee

Have you ever thrown a frisbee? Many kids and adults like to play with frisbees. Frisbees are made of plastic. They can be thrown far in the air. Some of the best frisbee players are dogs. They catch a frisbee in their mouths. Some dogs can jump nine feet in the air to catch a frisbee.

Check.

☐ Frisbees can be thrown far in the air.
☐ Frisbees have wings.
☐ Frisbees are made of plastic.

Circle.

Who likes to play with frisbees?

adults

kids

rabbits

dogs

Write.

Dogs catch frisbees in their _____.
paws   mouths

Color.

dog - brown   **frisbee** - blue

• Draw a picture of you and a friend throwing a red frisbee.

Learn About:

Football

Football is a fun game to watch or play. Players wear special uniforms. They wear pads to protect their bodies. They wear helmets to protect their heads. A football game is played with two teams. Each team tries to make a touchdown. Some players are good runners. Others can throw the ball well. It takes teamwork to win a football game.

Check.

☐ I wear a special uniform.
☐ I wear a helmet to protect my head.
☐ I am a baseball player.
☐ I wear pads to protect my body.

Circle.

How many teams play in a football game?

four
three
two

Unscramble.

Each team tries to make a _____.

w t c d u h o o n
8 1 4 6 3 5 2 7 9

Color.

Draw a brown football in the player's hands.

• Draw the football helmet of your favorite team.

Learn About:

Horseback Riding

Have you ever been horseback riding? Many people ride horses just for fun. Long ago, people rode horses to go from one place to another. They rode horses to hunt for food. They sat on horses without saddles. That was called riding bareback. Now people use a saddle to sit on a horse. Some people like to just trot along. Others like to gallop or even jump over fences on their horses.

Then

Now

Write.
   Many people ride _____ just for fun.
                        houses   horses

Check.
   Long ago, people rode horses . . .
      ☐ to go from one place to another.
      ☐ to chase cars.
      ☐ to hunt for food.

Circle.
   How can you ride a horse?   trot   gallop   cook

Match.
   bareback   now
   saddle   then

• Draw a horse jumping a fence.

Name_____

Learn About:

Hang Gliding

Hang gliding is an exciting sport. A glider looks like a big kite. The flier is strapped to the glider. The flier runs with the glider and jumps off a hill or cliff. Then, the wind begins to hold the glider in the air like a kite. The flier can move a bar to help the glider go up and down or sideways. Do you think hang gliding would be fun?

Circle.

A glider / glass looks like a big ketchup. / kite.

Write.

The flier is _____ to the glider.

stripe   strapped

Check.

The flier runs and jumps ☐ off a chair.
☐ off a hill or cliff.

Unscramble.

The _____ holds the glider in the air.

d n w i
4 3 1 2

Color.

1 - blue   2 - yellow

• Draw a picture of **you** hang gliding.

Learn About:

A Rodeo

Have you ever been to a rodeo? A rodeo has many different events. Cowboys and cowgirls perform for a crowd. They ride bucking horses and bulls. They have calf-roping contests. They ride bareback on horses. Prizes are given for the best person in each event. Some cowboys and cowgirls become famous in the rodeo.

Unscramble.

A _____ has many different events.
doroe
3 2 1 5 4

Circle.

Who performs in a rodeo?   cowboy   doctor   cowgirl

Check.

☐ We ride bucking horses and bulls.
☐ We rope calves.
☐ We rope fancy cars.
☐ We ride bareback on horses.

Circle.

Puzzles

Prizes   are given to the best person in each event.

• Draw a sign that tells all about the rodeo.

Name_____

Learn About:

Schools

A school is a place where people go to learn. Kids can learn math, spelling, science and reading. Many people go to special schools. Some of these schools teach people to be doctors and nurses. Some teach art and music. Schools help people become what they want to be.

Write.

A _____ is a place to _____.

    school   road   people   learn

Write.

| Math | Science | Reading | Spelling |

Circle.

What do some special schools teach people to be?

doctors   artists   kitchens   nurses   musicians

Write **your** school's name on the school above.

• Draw a picture of **your** school.

Learn About:

Parks

A park is a place for people to enjoy being outside. Most parks have lots of trees and flowers. People can sit on benches or at picnic tables. Many parks have swings and slides for kids to play on. Some people go to the park for picnics. Some go to play. A park is a nice place to spend a pretty day.

Write.

A _____ is a nice place to enjoy being outside.

puddle   park

Check.

Which could you see growing in a park?

☐ trees
☐ octopus
☐ flowers

Write.

A - bench   B - picnic table   C - swing   D - slide

○   ○   ○   ○

Color.

p - red
a - yellow
r - blue
k - green

park

• Draw a picnic basket full of your favorite picnic foods.

Learn About:

Airports

An airport is a very busy place. It is where planes take off and land. People can buy plane tickets at an airport. Their bags are put in a special part of the plane. There are restaurants and gift shops in airports. Many airports have places for watching planes take off and land.

Check.

An airport is a place where planes

☐ shop.
☐ take off.
☐ land.

Write.

A take off
B land

Circle.

Yes or No

People can buy plane tickets at an airport.	Yes	No
Some airports have gift shops.	Yes	No
An airport is really a hotel.	Yes	No
People can watch planes take off .	Yes	No

Color the planes: **take off** - orange   **land** - green

• Draw a picture of where you would like to fly.

Learn About:

A Library

A library is a place that has many books to read. Libraries also have magazines, records and films. A library is a quiet place to sit and read. You can also check out books to take home. The person who helps you is a librarian. The librarian keeps the books in order. Do you like to go to the library?

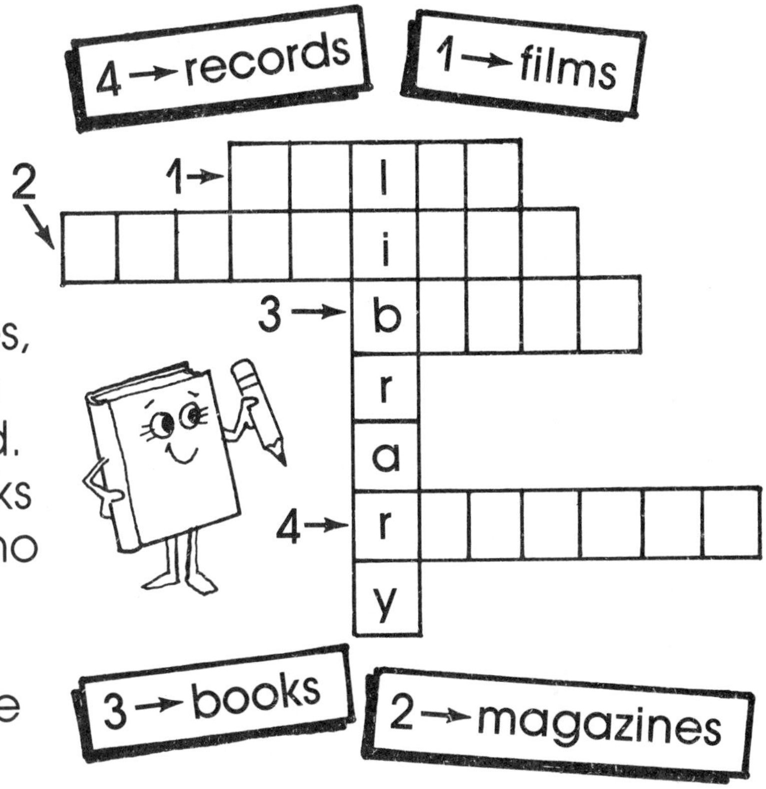

Name_____

4 → records   1 → films

1 → l i b r a r y
2 ↓
3 → b
4 → r

3 → books   2 → magazines

Write.

A _____ is a place that has many books.

listen   library

Write.   Libraries may have:

magazines
films
records

_____   _____   _____

Unscramble.

The person who helps you is a _____.

i b a i l a n r r
7 3 5 2 1 8 9 4 6

Check.

You can
☐ read at the library.
☐ cook at the library.
☐ check out books to take home.

Write each word in the puzzle.

• Write the names of your five favorite books.

Learn About:

A Post Office

A post office is a place that takes care of mail. People go to a post office to mail letters and packages. You can buy stamps there, too. Every letter and package is sorted at the post office. A postal carrier takes your mail to your mailbox. Some mail is sent to far away places by plane, train or truck.

Check.

What can people do at a post office?

☐ People can buy a hamburger.
☐ People can mail letters.
☐ People can mail packages.
☐ People can buy stamps.

Circle.

How is mail sent to far away places?

Who brings the mail to your mailbox? **(Circle in story.)**

Write **your** name and address on the envelope.

• Write a letter to **your** best friend.

Name_____

Learn About:

A Shopping Mall

Have you ever been to a shopping mall? A shopping mall is a group of stores. Many shopping malls have restaurants. Some even have movie theaters. Many shopping malls have one big roof over all the stores. Other shopping malls have an outside walkway. People like shopping malls because there is so much to see.

A - Clothes Shop
B - Movie Theater
C - Restaurant
D - Book Store

Write.

A shopping mall is a _____ of _____.

group   garden   stars   stores

Check.

Many shopping malls have
☐ restaurants.
☐ oceans.
☐ movie theaters.

Circle.

Which could you buy in most shopping malls?

Write the correct letter in each ◯ to name each store.

• Write a list of what you like to do in a mall.

Name_____

Learn About:

Police Officers

Police officers work hard to keep people safe. Their job is to make sure that people obey the laws. Police officers wear special uniforms. Some police officers ride in cars. Some ride on motorcycles. Some even ride in helicopters. Would you like to be a police officer?

Check.

☐ Police officers help keep people safe.
☐ Police officers put out fires.
☐ Police officers make sure people obey the laws.

Write.

Police officers wear special _____.

uniforms   laws

Circle.

What do some police officers ride in?

car

motorcycle

train

helicopter

Color.

uniforms - blue   **motorcycle** - red

• Draw a police officer flying in a helicopter.

Learn About:

Pilots

A pilot is a person who can fly an airplane. A pilot went to a special school to learn to fly a plane. Some pilots fly planes for fun. Some pilots fly planes as their jobs. A pilot sits in a special part of the plane called the cockpit. Have you ever seen a pilot sitting in the cockpit of a plane?

Write.

The person who flies an airplane is a _____.

point   pilot

Circle.

Yes or No

A pilot went to a special school.	Yes	No
Some pilots fly just for fun.	Yes	No
A pilot drives a school bus.	Yes	No
Some pilots fly planes as their jobs.	Yes	No

Circle.

Where does a pilot sit to fly an airplane?

 cockpit    bench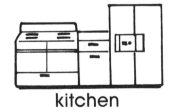
kitchen

Color.

Put green **X**'s on the pilots.

• Draw a picture of a cockpit with **you** as the pilot.

Learn About:

Fire Fighters

A fire fighter's job is to put out fires. This can be a very dangerous job. Fire fighters work at a fire station. When the alarm bell rings, the fire fighters rush to their truck. They drive to the fire. Fire fighters wear boots, hats and coats to protect themselves from the fire.

Check.

A fire fighter ☐ drives a bus.
☐ puts out fires.

Unscramble.

Fire fighters work at a _____ _____.

r f e i   t s n i a t o
3 1 4 2   2 1 7 5 3 4 6

Write.

1, 2, 3, 4.

◯ Fire fighters rush to their trucks.   ◯ They drive to the fire.

◯ They put out the fire.   ◯ The alarm bell rings.

Circle.

What do fire fighters wear to protect themselves?

  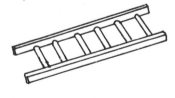 

Color the big picture: **boots** - black
coats - yellow
hats - red

• Draw a red fire truck.

Name_____

Learn About:

Farmers

Farmers have a very important job. They grow most of the food that we eat. Some farmers grow plants such as oats, corn and wheat. Some farmers raise animals for food. They sell milk from cows. They sell eggs from chickens. Many farmers use machines to help them do their work.

eggs   corn   milk

oats   wheat

w	g	m	i	l	k
h	x	e	s	c	l
e	t	g	x	o	i
a	m	g	p	r	v
t	v	s	g	n	b
y	x	o	a	t	s

Circle.

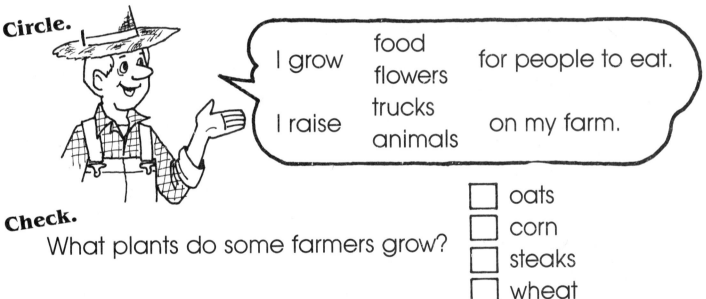

I grow   food   flowers   for people to eat.

I raise   trucks   animals   on my farm.

Check.

What plants do some farmers grow?

☐ oats
☐ corn
☐ steaks
☐ wheat

Match.

Which food comes from which animal?

milk   chickens

eggs   cows

Circle the words in the puzzle above.

• Draw a picture of three farm animals.

Learn About:

Doctors

Doctors help many people. They help sick people get well. They help healthy people stay well. People go to special schools to learn to be doctors. There are many kinds of doctors. There are doctors for children, eye doctors, ear doctors, bone doctors and heart doctors. Would you like to be a doctor?

1→bone

2↓eye

1→

2↓

d
o
c
t
o
r

3→

4→

3→heart

4→ear

Check.

How does a doctor help people?

☐ A doctor helps sick people get well.

☐ A doctor helps people build houses.

☐ A doctor helps healthy people stay well.

Unscramble.

There are many kinds of _____. Some doctors are

c t o d o s r
3 4 2 1 5 7 6

just for _____.

h d n c l e r i
2 5 8 1 4 7 6 3

Match.

eye doctor
ear doctor
bone doctor
heart doctor

Write.

Fill in the puzzle.

• Write a list of three things you do to stay healthy.

Learn About:

Astronauts

An astronaut is a person who travels in space. Only a few people can become astronauts. They must be in very good health. They must be very smart. There are special schools to train astronauts. Some astronauts are scientists. Some are pilots. They must work hard to be ready to travel in space.

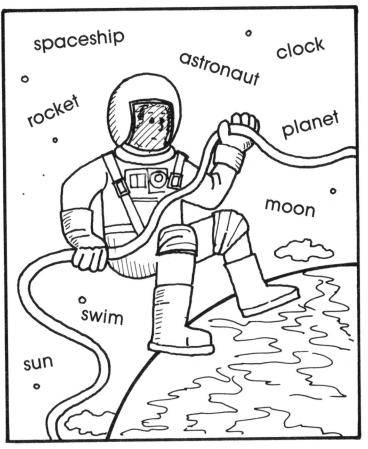

Unscramble.

A person who travels in space is an _____.

r t n o t s a u a
4 9 6 5 3 2 1 8 7

Check.

☐ Everyone can become an astronaut.

☐ An astronaut must be in very good health.

☐ An astronaut must be very smart.

☐ There are special schools to train astronauts.

Circle.

Some astronauts are: scientists
                       judges
                       pilots

Color.

Put a red circle around the **space** words.

• Draw a picture of where you would like to go in space.

Learn About:
A Stagecoach

People have not always had cars. A stagecoach was once used to go from one town to another. A **stagecoach** was a coach pulled by horses. Some fancy stagecoaches were pulled by six horses. A stagecoach carried people and mail. The stagecoach would change horses during a long trip. This would rest the horses.

20 MILES TO

Write. (Look at story.)

A _____ was a coach pulled by horses.

Circle.

Yes or No

A stagecoach would go from town to town.	Yes	No
A stagecoach was a new truck.	Yes	No
Some fancy stagecoaches had six horses.	Yes	No

Check.

What did a stagecoach carry?

☐ people
☐ animals
☐ mail

Color.

Two words are in **stagecoach**. Color: **first word** - red **second word** - blue

stage coach

Write the name of **your** town on the sign above.

• Draw a picture of a fancy stagecoach with six horses.

Learn About:

Helicopter

Would you like to ride in a helicopter? A helicopter flies in the air. It can fly **up** and **down**. It can fly **forward** and **backward**. It can fly **sideways**. A helicopter can even stay in one spot in the air! Helicopters can be many sizes. Some helicopters carry just one person. Some carry 30 people. Helicopters can be used for many jobs.

```
          h
1→ □ □ □ □ e □ □ □ □ □ □
          l
          i
2→    □ □ c □ □ □ □ □ □
 3→  □ □ o □ □
 4→  □ □ p □ □
          t
          e
5→   □ □ □ r □ □ □ □
```

Write.

A _____ flies in the air.

      trailer   helicopter

Write.

Which way can a helicopter fly? (Look at story.)

4→u __   3→d __ __ __   5→f __ __ __ __ __ __ __

2→b __ __ __ __ __ __ __   1→s __ __ __ __ __ __ __ __

Write the answers in the puzzle above.

Circle.

Yes or No

A helicopter can stay in one spot in the air.   Yes   No

Helicopters come in many sizes.   Yes   No

All helicopters can carry 10 people.   Yes   No

• Draw a big green helicopter.

Learn About:

A Taxi

A taxi is an automobile that someone must pay to ride in. The taxi driver picks people up and drives them where they want to go. Taxi drivers know a lot about their cities. They know many street names. They know how to go to the airport. They can find where people want to go. The taxi driver is paid at the end of the trip.

Unscramble.

A _____ is an automobile that you pay to ride in.
   a x i t
   2 3 4 1

Check.

☐ I am a taxi driver.
☐ I drive people where they want to go.
☐ I know the street names.
☐ A taxi is a bus.
☐ People pay me at the end of the trip.

Color.

t - blue
a - yellow
x - red
i - green

• Draw a red and blue taxi.

Learn About:

A Subway

Some big cities have a subway. A subway is a railroad that is under the ground. The trains carry people from one part of the city to another. The trains stop often to let people off and on. Many people ride to work on a subway. Others ride to school or to go shopping. Subways are nice because they do not take up space in a city.

Write.

A _____ is a railroad that is under the ground.

shop   subway

Circle.

Yes or No

The subway takes people to parts of the city.	Yes	No
The subway stops only one time each day.	Yes	No
The subway stops to let people off and on.	Yes	No

Circle.

Where are some people on the subway going?

 work    sleep    school    shopping

Color the subway train red.

• Draw where **you** would go on the subway.

Learn About:

A Spaceship

Would you like to blast off in a spaceship? A spaceship is made to carry people into space. A rocket is used to lift the spaceship from Earth. Computers help control the spaceship. Spaceships have different sections called modules. The command module is where astronauts live and work on a spaceship.

Check.
A spaceship is made
☐ to look at the moon.
☐ to carry people into space.

Write.
A _____ lifts the spaceship from Earth.
       ride   rocket

Check.
What helps control a spaceship?
☐ gas
☐ computers

Write.
A spaceship has different sections called _____.
                                          d o u l e s m
                                          3 2 4 5 6 7 1

Underline in story.
Where do the astronauts live and work?

Color the spaceship red.

• Draw a picture of **you** in a command module.

Learn About:

Dolphins

Dolphins are very smart animals. They can be trained to do tricks. Dolphins live in the water, but they are not fish. They are mammals. People are mammals, too. Dolphins must have air to live. They come to the top of the water to get air. Dolphins are fast swimmers. Some can swim 50 miles an hour!

Unscramble.

_____ are very smart animals.

o p h D i l s n
2 4 5 1 6 3 8 7

Circle.

Yes or No

Dolphins live in the water, but they are not fish.	Yes	No
Dolphins and people are mammals.	Yes	No
Dolphins like to live on land.	Yes	No
Dolphins must have air to live.	Yes	No

Circle.

Dolphins are fast   swimmers.
                       skaters.

Color a gray dolphin jumping into the hoop.

• Draw a dolphin swimming in the ocean.

Learn About:

A Kangaroo

A kangaroo is a furry animal that hops on its back legs. Its front legs are very short. Kangaroos can hop very fast. Some can move as fast as a car. Kangaroos have pouches on their stomachs. A baby kangaroo lives in its mother's pouch. The mother can carry her baby everywhere she goes.

Check.

☐ I am a furry animal.
☐ I hop on my back legs.
☐ My front legs are very long.
☐ I can hop very fast.

Write.

Kangaroos have _____ on their stomachs.
            pouches   purses

Circle.

A baby kangaroo lives   in a tent.
                        in its mother's pouch.

Color.

Draw a brown baby kangaroo in the pouch.

• Draw a kangaroo hopping.

Learn About:

Glassfish

Do you know how the glassfish got its name? The glassfish looks like it is made of glass. You can see all the way into a glassfish. You can even see its bones! A glassfish is a small fish that lives in the ocean. Some people have a glassfish for a pet. Would you like a pet glassfish?

Unscramble.

A _____ is a small ocean fish.

s f h i s l g s a
4 6 9 7 5 2 1 8 3

Circle.

Yes or No

A glassfish is full of water.	Yes	No
You can see into a glassfish.	Yes	No
Some people have glassfish for pets.	Yes	No

Circle.
Which is a glassfish?

Check.

You can even see my ☐ friends.
☐ bones.

Color the glassfish yellow.

• Draw four glassfish swimming in the ocean.

Learn About:
Whales

The whale is the largest animal on Earth. A whale looks like a giant fish. But, did you know that whales are not fish? They are mammals. They have lungs to get air, just like people. Whales live in the ocean. The largest whale is the blue whale. A group of whales is called a herd.

Unscramble.

The _____ is the _____ animal on Earth.

l e w a h   g t a l e s r

4 5 1 3 2   4 7 2 1 5 6 3

Circle.

What is a whale?   fish   mammal   turtle

Check.

What do whales and people have?

☐ jackets
☐ lungs
☐ fins

Circle.

Where do whales live?   ocean   cave   river

Match.

group of whales   blue whale

largest whale   herd

Color the whale blue.

• Draw a herd of whales in the ocean.

Name_____

Learn About:

Polar Bears

Polar bears live in a cold and snowy land. They are covered with thick, white fur. The fur helps keep them warm. Polar bears are tall and strong. They can be nine feet tall. They are good swimmers, too. They like to catch fish and seals. The white polar bear is hard to see on the white snow. How do you think this helps the polar bear?

Write.

Polar bears live in a _____ and _____ land.
                   hot   cold   snowy   dry

Check.

☐ Polar bears are covered with thick, white fur.
☐ Polar bears are not good swimmers.
☐ Polar bears are tall and strong.

Circle.

What do polar bears like to catch?

 fish
 camel
 seal

Put an **X** on the things that do not belong above.

• Draw a polar bear swimming in icy water.

Learn About:

Penguins

Do you think that all birds can fly? A penguin is a bird that cannot fly. Penguins stand on their back legs. Their walk looks like a waddle. Penguins have short, thick feathers. Their front is white. Their back is black. Penguins live mostly in cold oceans. They are very good swimmers.

Circle.

Yes or No

All birds can fly.	Yes	No
A penguin is a bird that cannot fly.	Yes	No
Penguins stand on their back legs.	Yes	No
Penguins live mostly in cold oceans.	Yes	No

Write.

A penguin's feathers are _____ and _____.
　　　　　　　　　　　　　long　short　　　thick　thin

Write.

Penguins are good ☐ sailors.
　　　　　　　　　　☐ swimmers.

Color.

Color the penguins: **1** - white　　**2** - black

• Draw three penguins swimming in a cold ocean.

Learn About:

A Hippopotamus

Have you ever seen a hippopotamus at the zoo? A hippopotamus is the third largest land animal. Even a baby hippopotamus can be 100 pounds! A hippopotamus lives near a river, pond or lake. A hippopotamus is a good swimmer. It stays in the water much of the time.

Circle.

A hippopotamus is the   second   largest land animal.
                         third

Check.

A baby hippopotamus can be   ☐ tiny and cute.
                               ☐ 100 pounds.

Circle.

A hippopotamus likes to live near a:

river   town   lake   theater   pond

Unscramble.

A hippopotamus is a good _____.

m i s w r m e
4 3 1 2 7 5 6

Color.

h - red
i - yellow
p - green
p - blue
o - purple

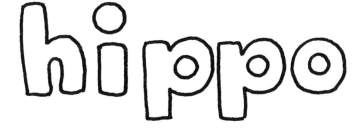

• Draw a baby hippopotamus in a river.

Learn About:

A Seahorse

Do you know how the seahorse got its name? A seahorse is a small fish. Its head looks like a horse! The seahorse has a long tail. It wraps its tail around sea plants. It waits for tiny sea animals to come by. A seahorse has no teeth, so it sucks up the tiny animals for food. A seahorse cannot swim fast. Sometimes it hides in the plants from big fish.

Unscramble.

The _____ is a small ocean fish.

a r o h s s e e
3 6 5 4 1 7 2 8

Check.

How did the seahorse get its name?

- ☐ It eats hay like a horse.
- ☐ Its head looks like a horse.

Circle.

Yes or No

The seahorse has no teeth.	Yes	No
The seahorse sucks up tiny animals.	Yes	No
The seahorse has a saddle.	Yes	No
The seahorse cannot swim fast.	Yes	No

Color the seahorse brown.

• Draw a picture of a make-believe "seadog".

Learn About:

Pelicans

A pelican is a large bird that lives near the water. A pelican has a large pouch under its bill. The pouch can hold water. A pelican also uses the pouch to catch fish. Pelicans can dive from the air into the water. They scoop up fish in their pouch. Pelicans are also strong fliers. Some pelicans can fly for hours without landing.

p
e
l
i
c
a
n

pouch   water   bird   bill   fish   dive   flier

Write.

1↓ I am a large b _ _ _.

2→ I live near the w _ _ _ _.

3→ I have a large p _ _ _ _.

4→ The pouch is under my b _ _ _.

5↓ I use the pouch to catch f _ _ _.

6→ I d _ _ _ from the air into the water.

7↓ I am a strong f _ _ _ _.

Write each answer in the puzzle above.

• Draw a pelican diving for fish.

Learn About:

Wolves

Do you think that wolves and dogs look a lot alike? They are really relatives. They even sound alike when they bark and howl. Wolves are covered with thick fur. They live on the plains and in forests. Wolves are very smart animals. A group of wolves is called a pack. Wolves eat mostly mice, rabbits and squirrels.

Circle.

Yes or No

Wolves and dogs are relatives.	Yes	No
Wolves and dogs bark and howl alike.	Yes	No
Wolves are smaller than cats.	Yes	No
Wolves are very smart animals.	Yes	No

Check.

Where do most wolves live?

☐ plains
☐ ocean
☐ forests

Circle.

Wolves eat mostly:

 mice    ducks   rabbits    squirrels

Color the wolf gray.

• Draw a **pack** of wolves.

Learn About:

Sea Shells

Have you ever found sea shells on a beach? Most of the shells you find are empty. But, once those shells covered certain ocean animals. Clams, oysters and snails are covered with shells. Scallops and mussels have shells, too. Many of these animals are eaten by other ocean animals. Their empty shells wash to the sand. Sea shells can be many sizes and colors.

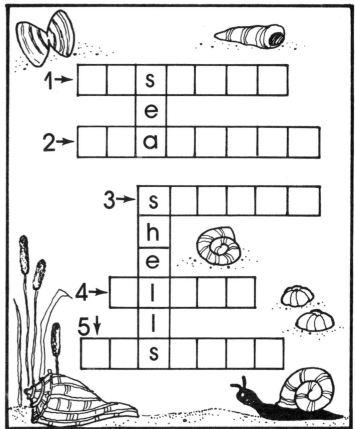

Circle.

Sunshine

Sea shells   cover some ocean animals.

Check.

Most of the sea shells you find are

☐ cute.

☐ empty.

snails	mussels	oysters	scallops	clams

Write.

1   o _ _ _ _ _ _   2 s _ _ _ _ _ _ _

3 s _ _ _ _ _   4   c _ _ _ _

5   m _ _ _ _ _ _

Write each word in the puzzle.

• Draw sea shells on a beach.

Learn About:

A Hummingbird

The hummingbird is the smallest bird in the world. It can fly very fast. It can fly up and down. It can even fly backwards! The wings of a hummingbird move so fast that they make a sound. It is a humming sound. That is how the hummingbird got its name. Have you ever heard a hummingbird?

Write.

The hummingbird is the _____ bird in the world.

smallest   tallest

Circle.

The hummingbird can   fly very fast.
                        eat very fast.

Circle.

Yes or No

The hummingbird can fly up and down.   Yes   No

The hummingbird can fly upside down.   Yes   No

The hummingbird can fly backwards.   Yes   No

Check.

How did I get my name?
☐ I like to hum and sing songs.
☐ My fast wings make a humming sound.

• Draw three hummingbirds flying together.

Answer Key

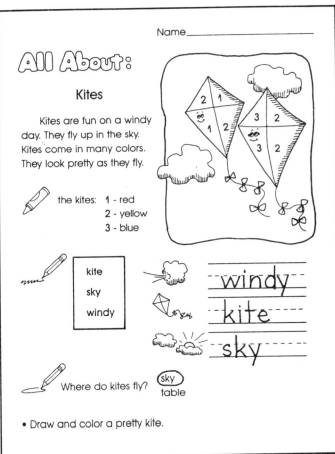

All About:

Kites

Kites are fun on a windy day. They fly up in the sky. Kites come in many colors. They look pretty as they fly.

the kites: 1 - red
2 - yellow
3 - blue

kite
sky
windy

windy
kite
sky

Where do kites fly? (sky) table

• Draw and color a pretty kite.

Page 1

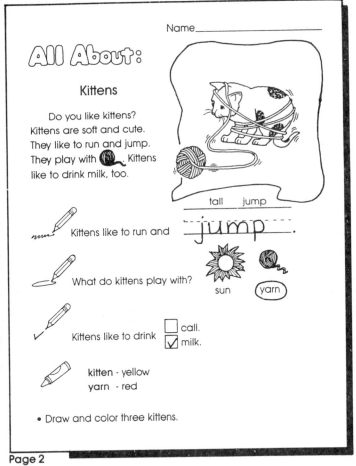

All About:

Kittens

Do you like kittens? Kittens are soft and cute. They like to run and jump. They play with 🧶. Kittens like to drink milk, too.

tall   jump

Kittens like to run and jump.

What do kittens play with?   sun   (yarn)

Kittens like to drink ☐ call.
☑ milk.

kitten - yellow
yarn - red

• Draw and color three kittens.

Page 2

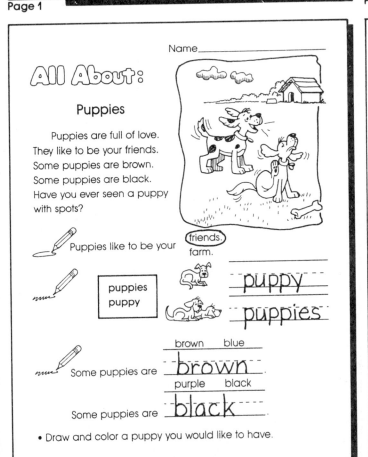

All About:

Puppies

Puppies are full of love. They like to be your friends. Some puppies are brown. Some puppies are black. Have you ever seen a puppy with spots?

Puppies like to be your (friends.) farm.

puppies
puppy

puppy
puppies

brown   blue
Some puppies are brown

purple   black
Some puppies are black

• Draw and color a puppy you would like to have.

Page 3

All About:

A Picnic

A picnic is fun on a sunny day. You can eat hot dogs, chips and lots of 🍉. Then, you can run and play games.

What day is good for a picnic?
green   games

It is fun to run and play games

a red hot dog in the bun.

five black seeds in the watermelon.

• Draw and color a picture of **yourself** at a picnic.

Page 4

Answer Key

All About:

Letters

Letters, letters, all around,
They go from A to Z.
Letters help you write your name.
They make each word you see.

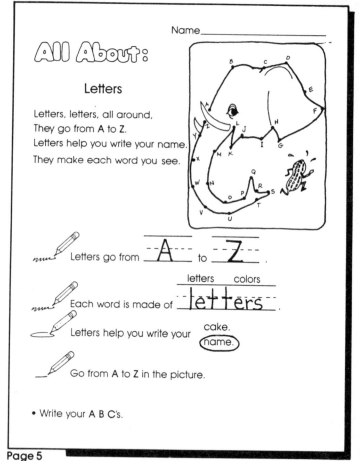

Letters go from __A__ to __Z__

Each word is made of ~~letters~~ colors __letters__

Letters help you write your cake. (name.)

Go from A to Z in the picture.

• Write your A B C's.

Page 5

All About:

Clouds

Clouds look pretty in the sky. They can be white and puffy. Clouds are made of water. That is where rain comes from. Rain comes from clouds.

Clouds look pretty in the ~~table.~~ (sky.)

| white | five | puffy |

Clouds can be __white__ and __puffy__

☑ I am made of water.
☐ I am a tree.
☑ I give you rain.

• Draw and color four clouds in a blue sky.

Page 6

All About:

Ice Cream

Ice cream is fun to eat on a hot day. You can have ice cream in a cone or dish. It comes in many yummy flavors. Which do you like best?

Ice cream is fun on a ~~hat hot~~ __hot__ day.

Draw two 🍦's of ice cream in the cone.
Draw three 🍦's of ice cream in the dish.

the ice cream picture: 1-brown, 2-pink, 3-yellow

• Draw a cone filled with ice cream you like the best.

Page 7

All About:

Pets

It is fun to have a pet. Dogs and cats are good pets. Birds and rabbits can be pets, too. Pets are good friends. They need care and love every day.

Pets are good ~~friends fast~~ __friends__

Pets need care and long. (love.)

| dog | rabbit | cat | bird |

__dog__   __bird__
__cat__   __rabbit__

• Draw and color a picture of your pet.

Page 8

Answer Key

All About:

Stars

Do you see the stars at night? They shine in the sky. The stars look very small. That is because they are so far away.

✏️ You can see the stars at ~~train.~~ (night.)

✏️ The stars _shine_ in the sky.
   (shine   saw)

✔️ Why do the stars look so small?
   ☑️ They are far away.
   ☐ They are happy.

🖍️ ___ the stars yellow.

• Draw and color five yellow stars.

All About:

The Sun

You can see the sun in the daytime. It looks round and yellow. The sun is a big star. It gives us light. It helps keep us warm.

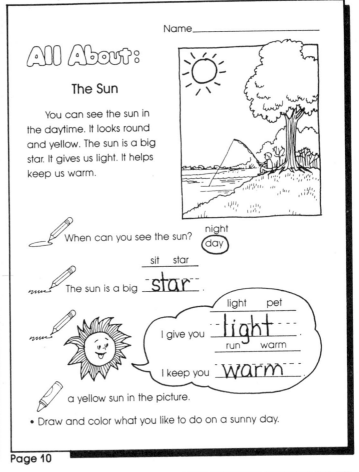

✏️ When can you see the sun? ~~night~~ (day)

✏️ The sun is a big _star_
   (sit   star)

🖍️ I give you _light_
   (light   pet) (run   warm)
   I keep you _warm_

🖍️ ___ a yellow sun in the picture.

• Draw and color what you like to do on a sunny day.

All About:

A Farm

A farm is a home for some animals. Horses, cows and pigs live on a farm. Sheep and chickens are farm animals, too. Many farm animals live in a big barn.

✏️ Which animals live on a farm?

✏️ A _farm_ is a home for some animals.
   (ride   farm)

🖍️ Many farm animals live in a big

 barn.

• Draw and color two farm animals.

All About:

A Birthday

Every year you have a birthday. You are one year older. It is fun to have a birthday party and a cake. The 🕯️🕯️🕯️ on the cake tell how old you are.

✏️ Every year you have a (birthday.) ~~barn.~~

✏️ It is fun to have a birthday _party_
   (party   puppy)

✏️ What can tell how old you are?

(candles)   balloon

🖍️ blue 🕯️🕯️🕯️ on the cake to tell how old you are.

• Draw and color a big birthday cake just for you.

Answer Key

All About:

Summer Camp

There is much to do at summer camp. You can swim and hike. You can ride in a 🛶. At night, you can sit around the fire and sing.

✏️ There is much to do at summer __camp__

house   camp

✏️
sing   hike   swim

🛶 __canoe__   🎵 __sing__

🏊 __swim__   🥾 __hike__

🖍️ the 🔥 red.

• Draw a picture of **yourself** at summer camp.

Page 13

All About:

Shapes

There are shapes all around us. A box can be ☐. A party hat can be like a △. A ball is a ○. A kite can be like a ◇. What is like a ▭ ?

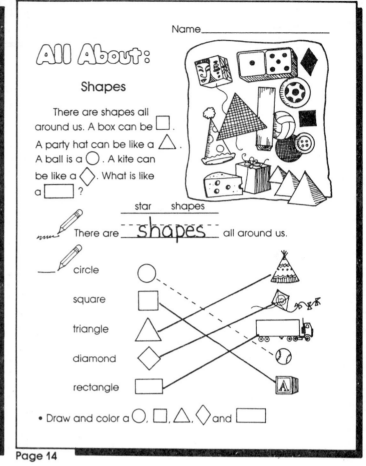

✏️ There are __shapes__ all around us.

star   shapes

___ circle ○

square ☐

triangle △

diamond ◇

rectangle ▭

• Draw and color a ○, ☐, △, ◇ and ▭

Page 14

All About:

School

Going to school helps you learn many things. You learn to read and write and spell. Your teacher helps you learn math, too. You will make new friends at school.

✏️ You learn new things at
step.
(school.)

✏️
read
spell
math
write

$+\frac{2}{3}{5}$ __math__

✏️ __write__

📖 __read__

📄 __spell__

✏️ your name on the ▦.

• Draw and color a picture of **your** school.

Page 15

All About:

Cowboys

A cowboy lives on a ranch. He takes care of cattle. He rides horses. A cowboy wears a big hat and tall boots. He works very hard.

🖊️ A cowboy lives on a (ranch.)
ride.

🖊️ A cowboy takes care of __cattle__

bugs   cattle

🖊️
☑ I ride a horse.
☑ I wear a big hat.
☐ I live in the city.
☑ I wear tall boots.

🖍️ the horse brown.

• Draw and color a picture of a cowboy.

Page 16

All About:

Friends

A friend is someone you like very much. Friends play together. Friends help each other, too. It is nice to have many friends.

A __friend__ is someone you like.

friend   from

Yes or No

Friends play together.   (Yes)   No
Friends are cars.   Yes   (No)
Friends help each other.   (Yes)   No

Which are friends?

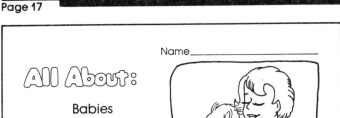

• Draw and color a picture of you and your friends.

All About:

Feelings

People can have many feelings. They can be happy. They can be sad. Sometimes people can feel angry. Everyone has feelings.

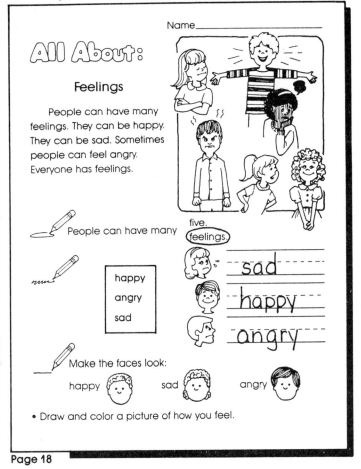

People can have many (feelings).

five.

happy
angry
sad

sad
happy
angry

Make the faces look:

happy   sad   angry

• Draw and color a picture of how you feel.

All About:

Babies

Everyone begins as a baby. A baby needs love and care. Sometimes babies cry when they are hungry. Babies like to drink lots of milk.

cook   baby

Everyone begins as a __baby__.

Yes or No

A baby needs love and care.   (Yes)   No
A baby is very tall.   Yes   (No)
Sometimes babies cry.   (Yes)   No
Babies like to drink milk.   (Yes)   No

b - red
a - yellow
b - blue
y - green

baby

• Draw and color a picture of **yourself** as a baby.

All About:

Names

Everyone has a name. Pets have names, too. Most people have a first name and a last name. Some people have a middle name. Do you?

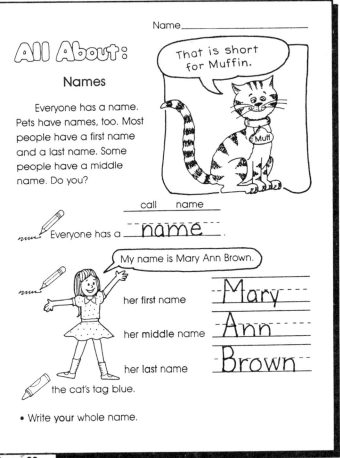

That is short for Muffin.

call   name

Everyone has a __name__.

My name is Mary Ann Brown.

her first name   Mary

her middle name   Ann

her last name   Brown

the cat's tag blue.

• Write **your** whole name.

Answer Key

Shopping

People go shopping for many things. You can shop for food. You can shop for clothes. It is lots of fun to shop for new toys.

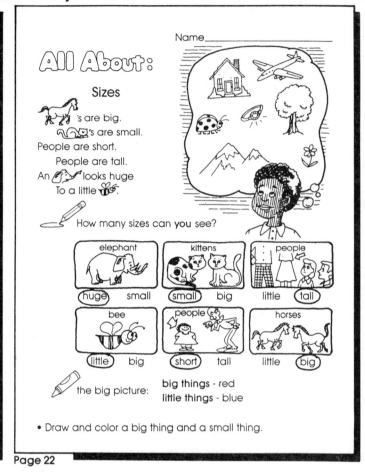

shopping   bus

People go _shopping_ for many things.

What can you shop for?

☑ You can shop for food.
☑ You can shop for clothes.
☐ You can shop for rain.
☑ You can shop for toys.

food - green   clothes - red   toys - yellow

• Draw and color what you would like to shop for.

Page 21

All About:

Sizes

🐎's are big.
🐛's are small.
People are short.
People are tall.
An 🐊 looks huge
To a little 🐝.

How many sizes can you see?

elephant	kittens	people
(huge) small	small big	little (tall)

bee	people	horses
(little) big	(short) tall	little (big)

the big picture: big things - red
little things - blue

• Draw and color a big thing and a small thing.

Page 22

All About:

A Bus

A bus can take you many places. Some kids ride to school on a bus. People can ride to work on a bus. A bus can even take you to another city.

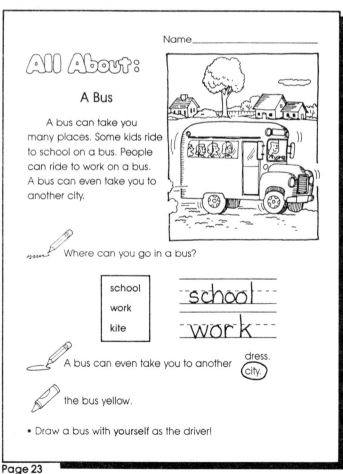

Where can you go in a bus?

school
work
kite

school
work

A bus can even take you to another   dress.
(city.)

the bus yellow.

• Draw a bus with yourself as the driver!

Page 23

All About:

Trucks

Trucks can carry lots of things. They can take food to the store. They can help you move to a new house. Trucks work very hard.

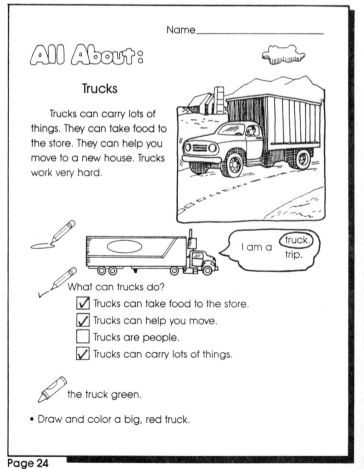

I am a (truck.)
trip.

What can trucks do?

☑ Trucks can take food to the store.
☑ Trucks can help you move.
☐ Trucks are people.
☑ Trucks can carry lots of things.

the truck green.

• Draw and color a big, red truck.

Page 24

Answer Key

All About: Trains

Have you ever been on a train? A train rides on tracks. The engine pulls the train. Many trains have a red [caboose] at the end.

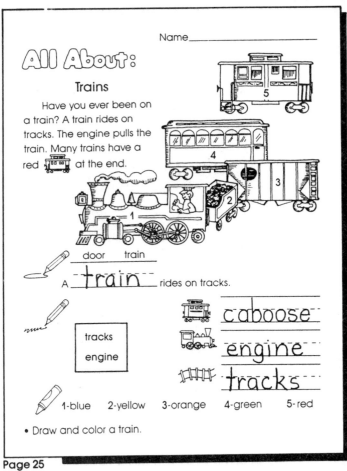

door **train**

A **train** rides on tracks.

tracks
engine

caboose
engine
tracks

1-blue 2-yellow 3-orange 4-green 5-red

• Draw and color a train.

Page 25

All About: Cars

Many people drive cars. A car helps you go places. You can ride in a car to places in your city. It is fun to go on a long car trip, too.

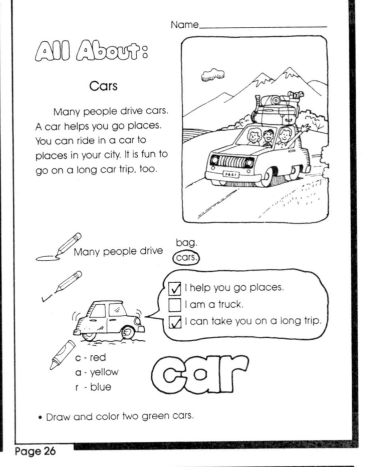

Many people drive (cars). bag.

☑ I help you go places.
☐ I am a truck.
☑ I can take you on a long trip.

c - red
a - yellow
r - blue

car

• Draw and color two green cars.

Page 26

All About: Airplanes

It is fun to fly in an airplane. Airplanes fly high in the sky. You can look out the window and see the clouds. You can look down and see a city.

Airplanes fly high in the (sky). hall.

What can you see from an airplane?

clouds
talk
city

clouds
city

two clouds in the picture.

• Draw and color a blue airplane.

Page 27

All About: Boats

There are many kinds of boats. Some boats have sails. A sailboat moves with the wind's help. Some boats have motors. They can go very fast.

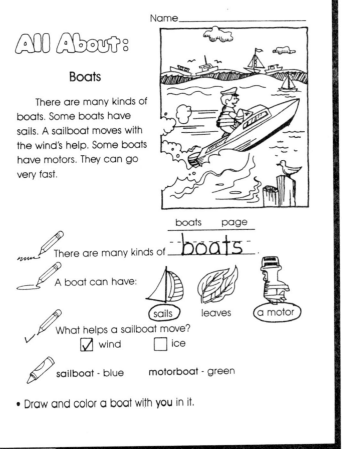

boats page

There are many kinds of **boats**

A boat can have:

(sails) leaves (a motor)

What helps a sailboat move?
☑ wind ☐ ice

sailboat - blue motorboat - green

• Draw and color a boat with **you** in it.

Page 28

Reading Comprehension IF8707   109   © 1990 Instructional Fair, Inc.

Answer Key

Page 29

Name_____

All About:

Clowns

Clowns are funny to watch. They like to make you laugh. They wear funny clothes. They do lots of tricks. Clowns like to give balloons and candy to kids.

 Clowns like to make you

laugh   cry

__laugh__.

Yes or **No**

Clowns wear funny clothes.   (Yes) No
Clowns do lots of tricks.   (Yes) No
Clowns fly in the sky.   Yes (No)
Clowns give balloons to kids.   (Yes) No

the clown.

• Draw and color a picture of **yourself** as a clown.

Page 29

Page 30

Name_____

All About:

Days

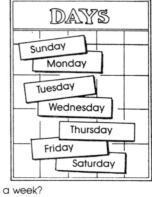

DAYS

Sunday
Monday
Tuesday
Wednesday
Thursday
Friday
Saturday

There are seven days in a week. Saturday and Sunday are the weekend days. You go to school the other five days. Which day do you like best?

How many days are in a week?

six   (seven)   ten

Which two days make a weekend?

| Saturday |
| Thursday |
| Sunday |

__Saturday__
__Sunday__

the five days you go to school.

• Draw and color what you do on a weekend.

Page 30

Page 31

Name_____

All About:

Trees

There are many kinds of trees. Some trees grow fruit. Some trees have flowers on them. Trees can be very tall. They need sun and water to grow.

There are many kinds of

fast.
(trees.)

What can grow on trees?

What do trees need to grow?
☑ sun
☐ sleep
☑ water

five red apples on the tree.

• Draw and color a green tree.

Page 31

Page 32

Name_____

All About:

Fruit

Do you like to eat fruit? Fruit is good for you. , apples and are kinds of fruit. Oranges and are fruit, too. Which fruit do you like the best?

There are many kinds of

fall   fruit

__fruit__

Which foods are fruit?

(banana)   (grapes)   (apple)

(orange)   steak   (pear)

the fruit in the basket:
1 - red   2 - green   3 - purple
4 - orange   5 - yellow

• Draw and color the fruit **you** like best.

Page 32

Answer Key

Page 33

All About:

Basketball

Some basketball players are very tall. They run and bounce the ball. They throw the ball into the net. They want to win the game.

Name_____

Some basketball players are very — small. / (tall.)

throw
bounce

bounce
throw

the basketball brown.

• Draw and color a basketball player.

Page 34

All About:

Swimming

Swimming is fun on a hot day. You can swim in a pool. You can go to the beach and swim in the ocean. The water helps you feel cool.

Name_____

swim   way

It is fun to **swim** on a hot day.

Where can you swim?

The water helps you feel — ☐ hot. / ☑ cool.

• Draw and color a picture of where you like to swim.

Page 35

All About:

Baseball

A baseball game is fun to watch. You can eat a hot dog and 🥤. You can yell and cheer. You may see your team hit a home run!

Name_____

pet   game

A baseball **game** is fun to watch.

You can eat:

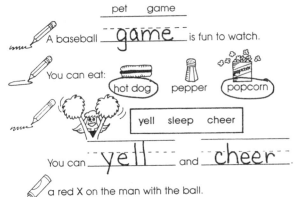

hot dog   pepper   popcorn

yell   sleep   cheer

You can **yell** and **cheer**.

a red X on the man with the ball.

• Draw and color a baseball and bat.

Page 36

All About:

Soccer

Do you know how to play soccer? You run and kick the ball. You can hit the ball with your head. But, you cannot touch the ball with your hands!

Name_____

How to play Soccer

kick   sit

1. Run and **kick** the ball.

mat   head

2. You can hit the ball with your **head**.

hands   dish

3. You cannot touch the ball with your **hands**

1 - red
2 - blue

• Draw and color a green and orange soccer ball.

111

Answer Key

All About: Spring

Name_____

It is warm in the spring. Flowers begin to bloom. Trees have new . Birds make their nests and lay eggs. Do you like to fly a kite in the spring?

It is ___warm___ in the spring.
(warm   last)

What can you see in the spring?

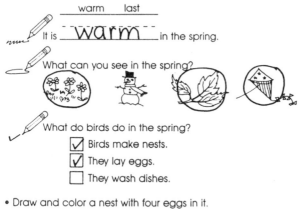

What do birds do in the spring?
- ☑ Birds make nests.
- ☑ They lay eggs.
- ☐ They wash dishes.

• Draw and color a nest with four eggs in it.

Page 37

All About: Autumn

Name_____

The air gets cool in the autumn. Kids go back to school. Animals store food for the winter. Leaves turn red, yellow and orange. It is a pretty time of the year.

The air gets ___cool___ in the autumn.
(time   cool)

What happens in the autumn?
- ☑ Kids go back to school.
- ☑ Animals store food.
- ☐ The air is very hot.

red   yellow   orange

• Draw and color an autumn tree.

Page 38

All About: Winter

Name_____

Winter can be cold and snowy. Animals stay near each other to keep warm. People wear coats, hats and . Kids can make a snowman. It is fun to play in the snow.

Winter can be:
- ☑ cold
- ☑ snowy
- ☐ purple

We try to stay ___warm___
(like   warm)

What do people wear in the winter?

gloves   hat   pan   coat

a black _____ on the _____

• Draw and color a snowman.

Page 39

All About: Birds

Name_____

Do you like to see birds fly? Some birds have pretty . Most birds like to live in trees. They eat seeds and worms and bugs.

Yes or No

Some birds have pretty feathers.   (Yes) No
Most birds live in trees.   (Yes) No
Birds live in tents.   Yes   (No)

What do birds like to eat?

seeds	worms	butter	bugs

___seeds___   ___worms___   ___bugs___

• Draw and color two birds.

Page 40

Answer Key

Page 41

All About:

Tigers

Tigers live in the jungle. They like to hunt for food at night. Tigers can climb trees. They can run fast. Tigers are very strong animals.

✎ Tigers live in the (jungle.) ~~table.~~

✎ store   night

Tigers like to hunt for food at **night**

✎ What can tigers do?

(climb trees)   cook   (run fast)

🖍 the tiger: **body - orange**   **stripes - black**

• Draw and color a tiger in a jungle.

Page 41

Page 42

All About:

Snakes

There are many kinds of snakes. Some snakes are very long. Some snakes are small. Snakes do not have legs. They crawl on the ground. They can move quickly.

✎ Yes or No
Snakes do not have legs.   (Yes) No
Snakes crawl on the ground.   (Yes) No
Snakes cannot move.   Yes (No)

✎ long   bird   small   **small**   **long**

🖍 the snakes green.

• Draw and color a long, brown snake.

Page 42

Page 43

All About:

Bats

Bats like to fly at night. They sleep in the daytime. A bat sleeps by hanging upside down. Most bats live in trees and caves. Have you ever seen a bat?

✎ night   noon

Bats like to fly at **night**

✎ Bats sleep in the room. (daytime.)

✎ How do bats sleep?

🖍 trees ☑
Most bats live in: caves ☑
floor ☐

🖍 the bats black.

• Draw and color a cave with sleeping bats in it.

Page 43

Page 44

All About:

Seals

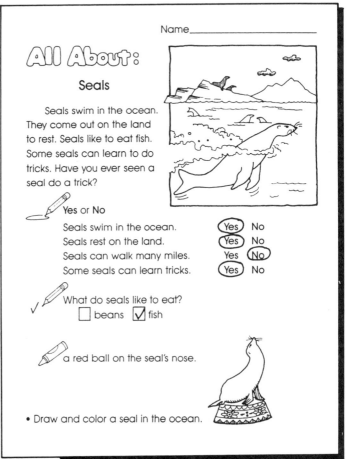

Seals swim in the ocean. They come out on the land to rest. Seals like to eat fish. Some seals can learn to do tricks. Have you ever seen a seal do a trick?

✎ Yes or No
Seals swim in the ocean.   (Yes) No
Seals rest on the land.   (Yes) No
Seals can walk many miles.   Yes (No)
Some seals can learn tricks.   (Yes) No

✓ What do seals like to eat?
☐ beans   ☑ fish

🖍 a red ball on the seal's nose.

• Draw and color a seal in the ocean.

Page 44

Answer Key

All About: Elephants

An elephant is a very large animal. Its long nose is called a trunk. The trunk takes food and water to the elephant's mouth. Would you like to ride on an elephant?

tiny   large

An elephant is a very **large** animal.

An elephant's nose is called a (trunk)/bag.

What can a trunk put in an elephant's mouth?
☑ food   ☐ boat   ☑ water

Make a trunk on the elephant.

• Draw and color a gray elephant.

All About: Giraffes

A giraffe is a very tall animal. It has a long, long neck. Giraffes can eat leaves from tall trees. They have long, thin legs. A giraffe has spots on its body. Have you ever seen a giraffe?

☑ I am very tall.
☑ I have a long, long neck.
☑ I have long, thin legs.
☐ I am very short.

spots   late

A giraffe has **spots** on its body.

the giraffe: **body** - yellow   **spots** - brown

• Draw and color a baby giraffe.

All About: Spiders

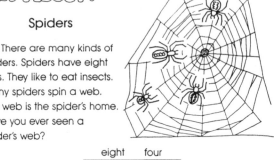

There are many kinds of spiders. Spiders have eight legs. They like to eat insects. Many spiders spin a web. The web is the spider's home. Have you ever seen a spider's web?

eight   four

Spiders have **eight** legs.

I spin a   week./(web.)

The web is my   kite./(home.)

What do spiders like to eat?
☑ insects
☐ jelly

8 black legs on this spider.
3 black spiders on the big web.

• Draw and color a spider and its web.

All About: Zebras

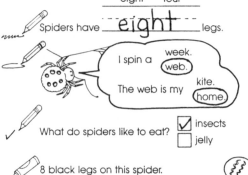

A zebra has a white body with black stripes. It looks much like a horse. Zebras like to eat grass. They can run very fast. Have you ever seen a zebra at the zoo?

black   red

A zebra has **black** stripes on its body.

A zebra looks much like a (horse.)/house.

What do zebras eat?
☐ gate
☑ grass

black stripes on the zebra.

• Draw and color a black and white zebra.

Answer Key

Page 49

All About: Turtles

Name_____

A turtle has a shell on its back. The shell is the turtle's home. A turtle can pull its head and legs into the shell. Some turtles live in the water. Some turtles live on the land. Have you ever seen a turtle?

Yes or No

A turtle has a shell on its back. (Yes) No
The shell is the turtle's home. (Yes) No
A turtle is very tall. Yes (No)

Where can turtles live?

| land | star | water |

__land__   __water__

the turtles green.

• Draw and color two turtles.

Page 49

Page 50

All About: Dinosaurs

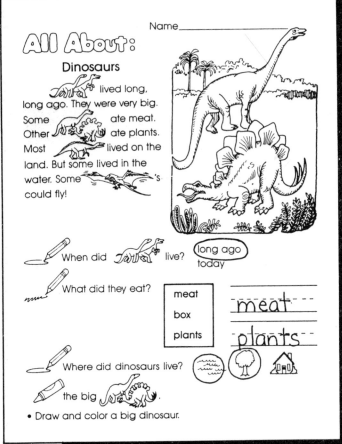

Name_____

_____ lived long, long ago. They were very big. Some _____ ate meat. Other _____ ate plants. Most _____ lived on the land. But some lived in the water. Some _____'s could fly!

When did _____ live? (long ago) today

What did they eat?

| meat |
| box |
| plants |

__meat__
__plants__

Where did dinosaurs live?

the big _____.

• Draw and color a big dinosaur.

Page 50

Page 51

Learn About: Colors

Making Colors

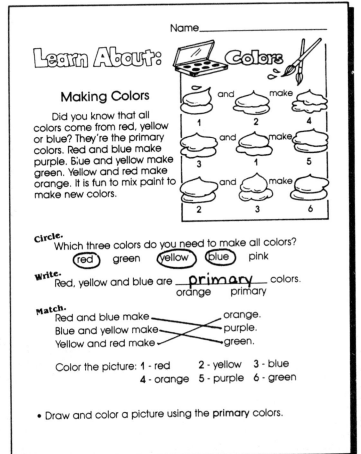

Name_____

Did you know that all colors come from red, yellow or blue? They're the primary colors. Red and blue make purple. Blue and yellow make green. Yellow and red make orange. It is fun to mix paint to make new colors.

Circle.
Which three colors do you need to make all colors?
(red) green (yellow) (blue) pink

Write. Red, yellow and blue are __primary__ colors.
orange primary

Match.
Red and blue make ———— orange.
Blue and yellow make ———— purple.
Yellow and red make ———— green.

Color the picture: 1 - red   2 - yellow   3 - blue
4 - orange   5 - purple   6 - green

• Draw and color a picture using the **primary** colors.

Page 51

Page 52

Learn About:

The Five Senses

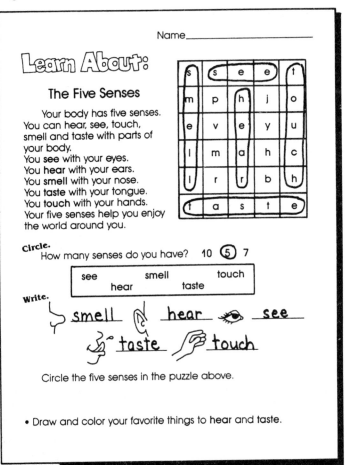

Name_____

Your body has five senses. You can hear, see, touch, smell and taste with parts of your body.
You **see** with your eyes.
You **hear** with your ears.
You **smell** with your nose.
You **taste** with your tongue.
You **touch** with your hands.
Your five senses help you enjoy the world around you.

Circle.
How many senses do you have? 10 (5) 7

| see | smell | touch |
| hear | taste | |

Write.
__smell__   __hear__   __see__
__taste__   __touch__

Circle the five senses in the puzzle above.

• Draw and color your favorite things to **hear** and **taste**.

Page 52

Answer Key

Page 53

Name_____

Learn About:

Months

There are twelve months in a year. The first month is January. The last month is December. Some months have 31 days. Some months have 30 days. February is the shortest month with 28 days. Can you name the months of the year?

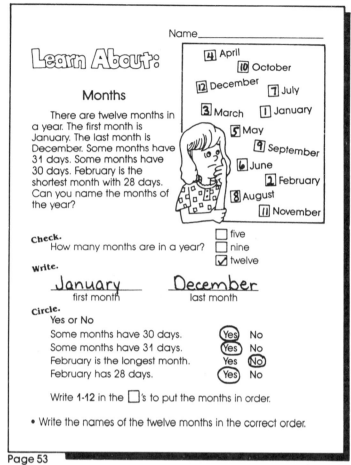

4 April	10 October
12 December	7 July
3 March	1 January
5 May	
9 September	
6 June	
2 February	
8 August	
11 November	

Check.
How many months are in a year?
☐ five
☐ nine
☑ twelve

Write.

__January__
first month

__December__
last month

Circle.
Yes or No

Some months have 30 days.	(Yes) No
Some months have 31 days.	(Yes) No
February is the longest month.	Yes (No)
February has 28 days.	(Yes) No

Write 1-12 in the ☐'s to put the months in order.

• Write the names of the twelve months in the correct order.

Page 53

Page 54

Name_____

Learn About:

Seasons

Every year has four seasons. Winter can be cold and snowy. In spring, flowers bloom and trees grow new leaves. Summer can be very hot. It is a good time for swimming and picnics. In autumn, the air gets cooler. Leaves fall from trees. Animals store food for the cold weather to come.

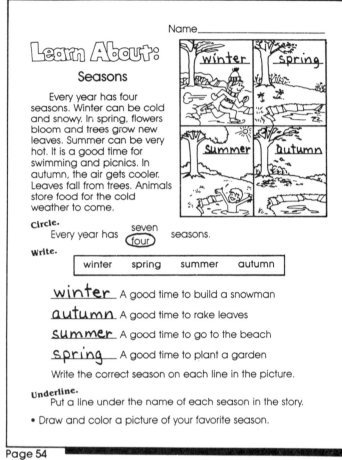

Circle.
Every year has ~~seven~~ (four) seasons.

Write.

| winter | spring | summer | autumn |

__winter__ A good time to build a snowman

__autumn__ A good time to rake leaves

__summer__ A good time to go to the beach

__spring__ A good time to plant a garden

Write the correct season on each line in the picture.

Underline.
Put a line under the name of each season in the story.

• Draw and color a picture of your favorite season.

Page 54

Page 55

Name_____

Learn About:

Weather

Weather is what it is like outside. Weather is always changing. There are many kinds of weather: hot, cold, rainy, snowy, foggy and stormy. Weather can be very helpful. Plants need sun and rain to live. Many animals need special weather, too. Polar bears like cold weather. Camels like hot weather. Which do you like best?

Circle.
Yes or No

Weather is what it is like outside.	(Yes) No
Weather is always the same.	Yes (No)
Plants need sun and rain.	(Yes) No

| hot | cold | rainy | snowy | foggy | stormy |

Write.

☀️: __hot__   ☁️ __foggy__   ⛄ __snowy__

🌧️ __stormy__   😣 __cold__   ☔ __rainy__

Color.
cold weather animal - white
hot weather animal - brown

• Draw and color a picture of your favorite weather.

Page 55

Page 56

Name_____

Learn About:

Money

Money has been used for many years to pay for things. Before people had money, they would trade one thing for another. Most people are paid money for their jobs. There are two kinds of money: paper money and coins. Can you count money?

Check.
Money is used to
☐ start a car.
☑ pay for things.

Underline.
What did people do before they had money?
People would trade one thing for another.
People would sing songs.

Circle.
Most people are paid (money) ~~salt~~ for their jobs.

Match.
paper money
coins

Color.
paper money - green   coins - gray

• Draw a picture of people trading things before they had money.

Page 56

Answer Key

Page 57

Learn About:
Time

There are many ways we measure time. A year is made of 365 days. A week has seven days. A day has 24 hours. An hour is made of 60 minutes. A minute is made of 60 seconds. A second goes very quickly. Can you blink your eyes in one second?

| day | year | minute | week | hour |

Write.

1 ↓ 36 days make a y **e a r**

2 → Seven days make a w **e e k**.

3 → 24 hours make a d **a y**.

4 → 60 minutes make an h **o u r**.

5 ↓ 60 seconds make a m **i n u t e**.

Write the answers in the puzzle above.

Check.
The words in the puzzle tell about ☐ money. ☑ time.

• Write a list of what you can do in **two** minutes.

Page 57

Page 58

Learn About:
Special Clothes

Many people need special clothes for their jobs. Uniforms are special clothes. Nurses, ball players and police officers wear uniforms. Costumes are special clothes, too. Clowns, actors and dancers wear costumes. Can you think of other kinds of special clothes?

Circle.
Many people need special clothes for their box. (jobs.)

| uniform | costume |

Write.

uniform — nurse   **costume** — dancer   **uniform** — police officer

costume — actor   **uniform** — ball player   **costume** — clown

Color. uniforms - blue   costumes - green

• Draw and color another uniform and costume.

Page 58

Page 59

Learn About:
A Hobby

A hobby is something special that a person enjoys doing. Some people collect things as a hobby. They may collect stamps, coins or even comic books! Some people build things as a hobby. They may build furniture or model airplanes. Other hobbies are reading, sports and gardening. Do you have a hobby?

Underline.
A hobby is
something you need to build houses.
something special that a person likes to do.

Write.
Some people **collect** things as a hobby.
                cover   collect

Circle.
What do some people collect?
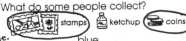 stamps   ketchup  coins   comic books

Circle.
Some people blue (build) things as a hobby.

Check.
They may build ☐ clouds. ☑ furniture. ☑ model airplanes.

• Write about **your** hobby.

Page 59

Page 60

Learn About:
Earth

Earth is a planet. It is the planet where we live. Earth has land and water. It gets light and heat from the sun. Earth has one moon. Many people think there is life on other planets. Earth is the only planet that we know has life. Do you think there is life on other planets?

Unscramble.
Earth is the **planet** where we live.
              l e t p n a
              2 5 6 1 4 3

Check.

☑ I have land and water.
☑ I get light and heat from the sun.
☐ I have five moons.
☑ I have one moon.
☑ I am a planet.

Circle.
Earth is the only planet that we know has stars. (life.)

Color.
Draw one yellow moon in the picture.

• Draw and color a picture of Earth.

Page 60

Answer Key

The Moon

Name_____

Do you ever look at the moon at night? The moon travels around the Earth. It gets its light from the sun. Men have gone to the moon in spaceships. They have walked on the moon. They even came back with moon rocks to study. Would you like to walk on the moon?

Circle.
The moon travels around the ~~room.~~ (Earth.)

Write.
The moon gets its light from the __sun__.
       Earth   sun

Check.
How did men go to the moon? ☑ spaceships
                             ☐ automobiles

Circle.
Yes or No
Men have walked on the moon. (Yes) No

Circle.
What did men bring back from the moon? ~~stars~~ (rocks)

Color.
Draw a red spaceship on the moon.

• Draw what you would do if you went to the moon.

Page 61

A Falling Star

Name_____

Have you ever seen a falling star? Falling stars are not really stars. They are small pieces of rock. As falling stars fall, they get hot and burn. They look big because they give off so much light. That is why they are so bright in the night sky. Did you know that meteor is another name for a falling star?

Circle.
Yes or No
A falling star is really a star.   Yes (No)
Falling stars are pieces of rock.   (Yes) No
Falling stars burn as they fall.   (Yes) No

Check.
Why does a falling star give off light?
  ☑ It gets hot and burns.
  ☐ It has a light bulb in it.

Unscramble.
Another name for a falling star is __meteor__.
                                    e r m o t e
                                    2 6 1 5 3 4

Color.
Draw two yellow falling stars in the picture.

• Write a poem about a falling star.

Page 62

Deserts

Name_____

A desert is very dry land that gets little rain. The air is very hot in the daytime. At night, the desert becomes very cool. Some deserts are made of sand. The wind blows the sand into little hills called sand dunes. Only a few plants and animals can live in the dry desert. Can you name a desert animal?

Circle.
Yes or No
A desert is very dry land.   (Yes) No
A desert has a lot of rain.   Yes (No)
A desert is hot in the daytime.   (Yes) No
A desert is cool at night.   (Yes) No

Write.
Some deserts are made of __sand__.
            sticks   sand

Circle.
Which are sand dunes?

Check.
Only a few plants and animals can live in the
  ☐ dirt.
  ☑ desert.

Color.
Draw a brown camel in the desert.

• Write a list of what you would need to travel in a desert.

Page 63

Oceans

Name_____

Have you ever seen an ocean? An ocean is a very large body of water. Our Earth has four oceans. They have special names: Atlantic Ocean, Pacific Ocean, Indian Ocean and Arctic Ocean. The Pacific Ocean is the largest ocean. It is two times larger than the Atlantic Ocean.

Check.
What is an ocean? ☐ A large farm
                   ☑ A large body of water

Circle.
How many oceans does the Earth have?
       seven (four) three

Write.
What are the names of the oceans? (Look at story.)

1↓ A t l a n t i c Ocean

2→ A r c t i c Ocean   3→ P a c i f i c Ocean

4↓ I n d i a n Ocean

Write the names in the puzzle above.

Circle.
Which ocean is the largest? Atlantic (Pacific)

• Draw a picture of what you would find deep in an ocean.

Page 64

Answer Key

Page 65

Learn About:

Mountains

Mountains can be found in many parts of the world. Mountains are much taller than hills. A group of mountains together is called a mountain chain. A mountain's highest point is called a summit. The highest mountain in the world is Mount Everest. Mount Everest is in Asia.

Circle.
Yes or No
Mountains are much taller than hills. (**Yes**) No

A or B
(A) summit (B) mountain chain

(**B**) A group of mountains together
(**A**) The highest point on a mountain

Unscramble.
The highest mountain in the world is Mount **Everest**.
vrEeset
2413657

Mount Everest is in **Asia**.
lAsa
3124

Color.
Draw a red ⚑ flag on the summit of the tallest mountain.

• Draw a mountain chain with five mountains.

Page 65

Page 66

Learn About:

Exercise

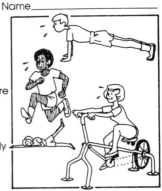

Do you like to exercise? Exercise is good for you. Walking and running are good ways to exercise. So are swimming and biking. Some people like to do push-ups, sit-ups and jumping jacks. Exercise can help you feel good. It can make your body stronger, too. What is your favorite kind of exercise?

Unscramble.
Exercise is good for you.
srEcxlee
74152638

Write.

walking
swimming
biking
running

 swimming walking
running biking

Check.
What do some people do for exercise?
☑ push-ups ☐ sleep ☑ jumping jacks ☑ sit-ups

Circle.
Yes or No
Exercise can help you feel good. (**Yes**) No
Exercise is very easy. Yes (**No**)
Exercise can make your body stronger. (**Yes**) No

• Draw a picture of you exercising.

Page 66

Page 67

Learn About:

Hiking

Have you ever gone hiking in the woods? Many people go on long hiking trips. They like to be outdoors. Hikers wear backpacks to carry what they need. They carry food and water. Most hikers use a compass to help them find their way. A compass tells which way they are going.

Underline.
Who would enjoy hiking?
People who don't like the outdoors.
People who enjoy being outdoors.

Write.
Hikers wear **backpacks** to carry what they need.
umbrellas backpacks

Write.
What could you find in a hiker's backpack?

water compass
water bike food

1. **water**
2. **food**
3. **compass**

Color.
the hikers' backpacks - brown the hikers' compasses - red

• Draw a picture of you hiking in the woods.

Page 67

Page 68

Learn About:

Skateboarding

Many kids like to ride skateboards. Skateboards are short boards on wheels. Some cities have special places to ride skateboards. They are called skateboard parks. The parks have rules to keep kids safe. Kids must wear helmets on their heads. They must also wear kneepads and gloves.

Circle.
Yes or No
Many kids like to ride skateboards. (**Yes**) No
Skateboards are used to build houses. Yes (**No**)
Skateboards are short boards on wheels. (**Yes**) No
Some cities have skateboard parks. (**Yes**) No

Write.
Skateboard parks have **rules** to keep kids safe.
jobs rules

gloves
helmets
kneepads

RULES
1. Kids must wear **helmets**.
2. Kids must wear **gloves** and **kneepads**

Color.
skateboards - red helmets - blue

• Draw and color a green skateboard.

Page 68

119

Answer Key

Learn About:

Frisbee

Name_____

Have you ever thrown a frisbee? Many kids and adults like to play with frisbees. Frisbees are made of plastic. They can be thrown far in the air. Some of the best frisbee players are dogs. They catch a frisbee in their mouths. Some dogs can jump nine feet in the air to catch a frisbee.

Check.
- ☑ Frisbees can be thrown far in the air.
- ☐ Frisbees have wings.
- ☑ Frisbees are made of plastic.

Circle.
Who likes to play with frisbees?

 adults   kids   rabbits   dogs

Write.
Dogs catch frisbees in their __mouths__
paws   mouths

Color.
dog - brown   frisbee - blue

• Draw a picture of you and a friend throwing a red frisbee.

Page 69

Learn About:

Football

Name_____

Football is a fun game to watch or play. Players wear special uniforms. They wear pads to protect their bodies. They wear helmets to protect their heads. A football game is played with two teams. Each team tries to make a touchdown. Some players are good runners. Others can throw the ball well. It takes teamwork to win a football game.

Check.

- ☑ I wear a special uniform.
- ☑ I wear a helmet to protect my head.
- ☐ I am a baseball player.
- ☑ I wear pads to protect my body.

Circle.
How many teams play in a football game?   four   three   ⨀two

Unscramble.
Each team tries to make a __touchdown__.
w t c d u h o o n
8 1 4 6 3 5 2 7 9

Color.
Draw a brown football in the player's hands.

• Draw the football helmet of your favorite team.

Page 70

Learn About:

Horseback Riding

Name_____

Then

Now

Have you ever been horseback riding? Many people ride horses just for fun. Long ago, people rode horses to go from one place to another. They rode horses to hunt for food. They sat on horses without saddles. That was called riding bareback. Now people use a saddle to sit on a horse. Some people like to just trot along. Others like to gallop or even jump over fences on their horses.

Write.
Many people ride __horses__ just for fun.
houses   horses

Check.
Long ago, people rode horses . . .
- ☑ to go from one place to another.
- ☐ to chase cars.
- ☑ to hunt for food.

Circle.
How can you ride a horse?   ⨀trot   ⨀gallop   cook

Match.
bareback ⟋ now
saddle ⟋ then

• Draw a horse jumping a fence.

Page 71

Learn About:

Hang Gliding

Name_____

Hang gliding is an exciting sport. A glider looks like a big kite. The flier is strapped to the glider. The flier runs with the glider and jumps off a hill or cliff. Then, the wind begins to hold the glider in the air like a kite. The flier can move a bar to help the glider go up and down or sideways. Do you think hang gliding would be fun?

Circle.
A ⨀glider glass looks like a big   ketchup. ⨀kite

Write.
The flier is __strapped__ to the glider.
stripe   strapped

Check.
The flier runs and jumps
- ☐ off a chair.
- ☑ off a hill or cliff.

Unscramble.
The __wind__ holds the glider in the air.
d n w l
4 3 1 2

Color.
1 - blue   2 - yellow

• Draw a picture of you hang gliding.

Page 72

Learn About:

A Rodeo

Have you ever been to a rodeo? A rodeo has many different events. Cowboys and cowgirls perform for a crowd. They ride bucking horses and bulls. They have calf-roping contests. They ride bareback on horses. Prizes are given for the best person in each event. Some cowboys and cowgirls become famous in the rodeo.

Unscramble.

A __rodeo__ has many different events.
  d o r o e
  3 2 1 5 4

Circle.
Who performs in a rodeo? (cowboy)   doctor   (cowgirl)

Check.

- ☑ We ride bucking horses and bulls.
- ☑ We rope calves.
- ☐ We rope fancy cars.
- ☑ We ride bareback on horses.

Circle.
Puzzles
(Prizes) are given to the best person in each event.

• Draw a sign that tells all about the rodeo.

Page 73

Learn About:

Schools

A school is a place where people go to learn. Kids can learn math, spelling, science and reading. Many people go to special schools. Some of these schools teach people to be doctors and nurses. Some teach art and music. Schools help people become what they want to be.

Write.
A __school__ is a place to __learn__
  school   road   people   learn

Write.

| Math | Science | Reading | Spelling |

Circle.
What do some special schools teach people to be?
(doctors) (artists)   kitchens   (nurses) (musicians)

Write your school's name on the school above.

• Draw a picture of your school.

Page 74

Learn About:

Parks

A park is a place for people to enjoy being outside. Most parks have lots of trees and flowers. People can sit on benches or at picnic tables. Many parks have swings and slides for kids to play on. Some people go to the park for picnics. Some go to play. A park is a nice place to spend a pretty day.

Write.
A __park__ is a nice place to enjoy being outside.
  puddle   park

Check.
Which could you see growing in a park?
- ☑ trees
- ☐ octopus
- ☑ flowers

Write.
A - bench   B - picnic table   C - swing   D - slide
Ⓑ   Ⓒ   Ⓓ   Ⓐ

Color.
p - red
a - yellow
r - blue
k - green

park

• Draw a picnic basket full of your favorite picnic foods.

Page 75

Learn About:

Airports

An airport is a very busy place. It is where planes take off and land. People can buy plane tickets at an airport. Their bags are put in a special part of the plane. There are restaurants and gift shops in airports. Many airports have places for watching planes take off and land.

Check.
An airport is a place where planes
- ☐ shop.
- ☑ take off.
- ☑ land.

Write.
Ⓐ   Ⓑ
A take off
B land

Circle.
Yes or No
People can buy plane tickets at an airport.   (Yes) No
Some airports have gift shops.   (Yes) No
An airport is really a hotel.   Yes (No)
People can watch planes take off.   (Yes) No

Color the planes: take off - orange   land - green

• Draw a picture of where you would like to fly.

Page 76

Answer Key

Learn About:
A Library

A library is a place that has many books to read. Libraries also have magazines, records and films. A library is a quiet place to sit and read. You can also check out books to take home. The person who helps you is a librarian. The librarian keeps the books in order. Do you like to go to the library?

4 → records   1 → films

```
2    1 → f i l m s
m a g a z i n e s
     3 → b o o k s
        r
        a
        r
4 → r e c o r d s
        y
```

3 → books   2 → magazines

Write.
A __library__ is a place that has many books.
listen   library

Write.   Libraries may have:
magazines
films
records   __films__   __magazines__   __records__

Unscramble.
The person who helps you is a __librarian__.
i b a l l a n r r
7 3 5 2 1 8 9 4 6

Check.
You can   ☑ read at the library.
          ☐ cook at the library.
          ☑ check out books to take home.

Write each word in the puzzle.

• Write the names of your five favorite books.

Page 77

Learn About:
A Post Office

A post office is a place that takes care of mail. People go to a post office to mail letters and packages. You can buy stamps there, too. Every letter and package is sorted at the post office. A postal carrier takes your mail to your mailbox. Some mail is sent to far away places by plane, train or truck.

Check.
What can people do at a post office?
☐ People can buy a hamburger.
☑ People can mail letters.
☑ People can mail packages.
☑ People can buy stamps.

Circle.
How is mail sent to far away places?

Who brings the mail to your mailbox? (Circle in story.)

Write your name and address on the envelope.

• Write a letter to your best friend.

Page 78

Learn About:
A Shopping Mall

Have you ever been to a shopping mall? A shopping mall is a group of stores. Many shopping malls have restaurants. Some even have movie theaters. Many shopping malls have one big roof over all the stores. Other shopping malls have an outside walkway. People like shopping malls because there is so much to see.

A - Clothes Shop
B - Movie Theater
C - Restaurant
D - Book Store

Write.
A shopping mall is a __group__ of __stores__.
group   garden   stars   stores

Check.
Many shopping malls have   ☑ restaurants.
                           ☐ oceans.
                           ☑ move theaters.

Circle.
Which could you buy in most shopping malls?

Write the correct letter in each ◯ to name each store.

• Write a list of what you like to do in a mall.

Page 79

Learn About:
Police Officers

Police officers work hard to keep people safe. Their job is to make sure that people obey the laws. Police officers wear special uniforms. Some police officers ride in cars. Some ride on motorcycles. Some even ride in helicopters. Would you like to be a police officer?

Check.
☑ Police officers help keep people safe.
☐ Police officers put out fires.
☑ Police officers make sure people obey the laws.

Write.
Police officers wear special __uniforms__.
                              uniforms   laws

Circle.
What do some police officers ride in?

car   motorcycle   train   helicopter

Color.
uniforms - blue   motorcycle - red

• Draw a police officer flying in a helicopter.

Page 80

Answer Key

Learn About:

Pilots

A pilot is a person who can fly an airplane. A pilot went to a special school to learn to fly a plane. Some pilots fly planes for fun. Some pilots fly planes as their jobs. A pilot sits in a special part of the plane called the cockpit. Have you ever seen a pilot sitting in the cockpit of a plane?

Write.
The person who flies an airplane is a __pilot__ .
point   pilot

Circle.
Yes or No
A pilot went to a special school.   (Yes)   No
Some pilots fly just for fun.   (Yes)   No
A pilot drives a school bus.   Yes   (No)
Some pilots fly planes as their jobs.   (Yes)   No

Circle.
Where does a pilot sit to fly an airplane?

cockpit   bench   kitchen

Color.
Put green X's on the pilots.

• Draw a picture of a cockpit with **you** as the pilot.

Page 81

Learn About:

Fire Fighters

A fire fighter's job is to put out fires. This can be a very dangerous job. Fire fighters work at a fire station. When the alarm bell rings, the fire fighters rush to their truck. They drive to the fire. Fire fighters wear boots, hats and coats to protect themselves from the fire.

Check.
A fire fighter   ☐ drives a bus.
                  ☑ puts out fires.

Unscramble.
Fire fighters work at a __fire__   __station__ .
r f e i   t s n l a t o
3 1 4 2   2 1 7 5 3 4 6

Write.
1, 2, 3, 4.
② Fire fighters rush to their trucks.   ③ They drive to the fire.
④ They put out the fire.   ① The alarm bell rings.

Circle.
What do fire fighters wear to protect themselves?

Color the big picture: **boots - black**
                          coats - yellow
                          hats - red

• Draw a red fire truck.

Page 82

Learn About:

Farmers

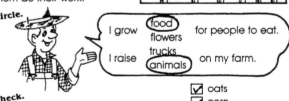

Farmers have a very important job. They grow most of the food that we eat. Some farmers grow plants such as oats, corn and wheat. Some farmers raise animals for food. They sell milk from cows. They sell eggs from chickens. Many farmers use machines to help them do their work.

Circle.

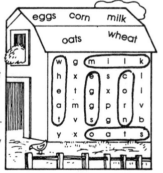
I grow (food) flowers for people to eat.
I raise trucks (animals) on my farm.

Check.
What plants do some farmers grow?
☑ oats
☑ corn
☐ steaks
☑ wheat

Match.
Which food comes from which animal?
milk ⤬ chickens
eggs ⤬ cows

Circle the words in the puzzle above.

• Draw a picture of three farm animals.

Page 83

Learn About:

Doctors

1→bone
2↓eye
1→bone
3→heart
4→ear
3→heart   4→ear

Doctors help many people. They help sick people get well. They help healthy people stay well. People go to special schools to learn to be doctors. There are many kinds of doctors. There are doctors for children, eye doctors, ear doctors, bone doctors and heart doctors. Would you like to be a doctor?

Check.
How does a doctor help people?
☑ A doctor helps sick people get well.
☐ A doctor helps people build houses.
☑ A doctor helps healthy people stay well.

Unscramble.
There are many kinds of __doctors__ . Some doctors are
c t o d o s r
3 4 2 1 5 7 6
just for __children__ .
h d n c l e r i
2 5 8 1 4 7 6 3

Match.
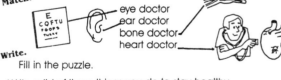
eye doctor
ear doctor
bone doctor
heart doctor

Write.
Fill in the puzzle.

• Write a list of three things you do to stay healthy.

Page 84

Answer Key

Learn About:

Astronauts

Name_____

An astronaut is a person who travels in space. Only a few people can become astronauts. They must be in very good health. They must be very smart. There are special schools to train astronauts. Some astronauts are scientists. Some are pilots. They must work hard to be ready to travel in space.

Unscramble.

A person who travels in space is an __astronaut__.
r t n o t s a u a
4 9 6 5 3 2 1 8 7

Check.
- ☐ Everyone can become an astronaut.
- ☑ An astronaut must be in very good health.
- ☑ An astronaut must be very smart.
- ☑ There are special schools to train astronauts.

Circle.

Some astronauts are: (scientists) judges (pilots)

Color.

Put a red circle around the **space** words.

• Draw a picture of where you would like to go in space.

Learn About:

A Stagecoach

Name_____

People have not always had cars. A stagecoach was once used to go from one town to another. A **stagecoach** was a coach pulled by horses. Some fancy stagecoaches were pulled by six horses. A stagecoach carried people and mail. The stagecoach would change horses during a long trip. This would rest the horses.

Write. (Look at story.)

A __stagecoach__ was a coach pulled by horses.

Circle.
Yes or No

A stagecoach would go from town to town. (Yes) No
A stagecoach was a new truck. Yes (No)
Some fancy stagecoaches had six horses. (Yes) No

Check.
What did a stagecoach carry?
- ☑ people
- ☐ animals
- ☑ mail

Color.
Two words are in **stagecoach**. Color: first word - red   second word - blue

stage coach

Write the name of **your** town on the sign above.

• Draw a picture of a fancy stagecoach with six horses.

Learn About:

Helicopter

Name_____

1→s i d e w a y s
2→b a c k w a r d
3→d o w n
4→u p
5→f o r w a r d

Would you like to ride in a helicopter? A helicopter flies in the air. It can fly up and down. It can fly forward and backward. It can fly sideways. A helicopter can even stay in one spot in the air! Helicopters can be many sizes. Some helicopters carry just one person. Some carry 30 people. Helicopters can be used for many jobs.

Write.
A __helicopter__ flies in the air.
trailer   helicopter

Write.
Which way can a helicopter fly? (Look at story.)

4→u p   3→d o w n   5→f o r w a r d
2→b a c k w a r d   1→s i d e w a y s

Write the answers in the puzzle above.

Circle.
Yes or No

A helicopter can stay in one spot in the air. (Yes) No
Helicopters come in many sizes. (Yes) No
All helicopters can carry 10 people. Yes (No)

• Draw a big green helicopter.

Learn About:

A Taxi

Name_____

A taxi is an automobile that someone must pay to ride in. The taxi driver picks people up and drives them where they want to go. Taxi drivers know a lot about their cities. They know many street names. They know how to go to the airport. They can find where people want to go. The taxi driver is paid at the end of the trip.

Unscramble.

A __taxi__ is an automobile that you pay to ride in.
a x i t
2 3 4 1

Check.
- ☑ I am a taxi driver.
- ☑ I drive people where they want to go.
- ☑ I know the street names.
- ☐ A taxi is a bus.
- ☑ People pay me at the end of the trip.

Color.
t - blue
a - yellow
x - red
i - green

taxi

• Draw a red and blue taxi.

Answer Key

Learn About:
A Subway

Name_____

Some big cities have a subway. A subway is a railroad that is under the ground. The trains carry people from one part of the city to another. The trains stop often to let people off and on. Many people ride to work on a subway. Others ride to school or to go shopping. Subways are nice because they do not take up space in a city.

Write.
A __subway__ is a railroad that is under the ground.
   shop   subway

Circle.
Yes or No

The subway takes people to parts of the city.   (Yes) No
The subway stops only one time each day.   Yes   (No)
The subway stops to let people off and on.   (Yes) No

Circle.
Where are some people on the subway going?

 work   sleep   school   shopping

Color the subway train red.

• Draw where you would go on the subway.

Page 89

Learn About:
A Spaceship

Name_____

Would you like to blast off in a spaceship? A spaceship is made to carry people into space. A rocket is used to lift the spaceship from Earth. Computers help control the spaceship. Spaceships have different sections called modules. <u>The command module is where astronauts live and work on a spaceship.</u>

Check.
A spaceship is made   ☐ to look at the moon.
                      ☑ to carry people into space.

Write.
A __rocket__ lifts the spaceship from Earth.
   ride   rocket

Check.
What helps control a spaceship?   ☐ gas
                                  ☑ computers

Write.
A spaceship has different sections called __modules__.
                                          d o u l e s m
                                          3 2 4 5 6 7 1

Underline in story.
Where do the astronauts live and work?

Color the spaceship red.

• Draw a picture of **you** in a command module.

Page 90

Learn About:
Dolphins

Name_____

Dolphins are very smart animals. They can be trained to do tricks. Dolphins live in the water, but they are not fish. They are mammals. People are mammals, too. Dolphins must have air to live. They come to the top of the water to get air. Dolphins are fast swimmers. Some can swim 50 miles an hour!

Unscramble.
__Dolphins__ are very smart animals.
o p h D l l s n
2 4 5 1 6 3 8 7

Circle.
Yes or No

Dolphins live in the water, but they are not fish.   (Yes) No
Dolphins and people are mammals.   (Yes) No
Dolphins like to live on land.   Yes   (No)
Dolphins must have air to live.   (Yes) No

Circle.
Dolphins are fast   (swimmers.)
                    skaters.

Color a gray dolphin jumping into the hoop.

• Draw a dolphin swimming in the ocean.

Page 91

Learn About:
A Kangaroo

Name_____

A kangaroo is a furry animal that hops on its back legs. Its front legs are very short. Kangaroos can hop very fast. Some can move as fast as a car. Kangaroos have pouches on their stomachs. A baby kangaroo lives in its mother's pouch. The mother can carry her baby everywhere she goes.

Check.

☑ I am a furry animal.
☑ I hop on my back legs.
☐ My front legs are very long.
☑ I can hop very fast.

Write.
Kangaroos have __pouches__ on their stomachs.
              pouches   purses

Circle.
A baby kangaroo lives   in a tent.
                        (in its mother's pouch.)

Color.
Draw a brown baby kangaroo in the pouch.

• Draw a kangaroo hopping.

Page 92

Answer Key

Learn About:
Glassfish

Name_____

Do you know how the glassfish got its name? The glassfish looks like it is made of glass. You can see all the way into a glassfish. You can even see its bones! A glassfish is a small fish that lives in the ocean. Some people have a glassfish for a pet. Would you like a pet glassfish?

Unscramble.

A _glassfish_ is a small ocean fish.
s f h i s l g s a
4 6 9 7 5 2 1 8 3

Circle.
Yes or No
A glassfish is full of water.   Yes (No)
You can see into a glassfish.   (Yes) No
Some people have glassfish for pets. (Yes) No

Circle.
Which is a glassfish?

Check.
You can even see my ☐ friends.
                      ☑ bones.

Color the glassfish yellow.

• Draw four glassfish swimming in the ocean.

Page 93

Learn About:
Whales

Name_____

The whale is the largest animal on Earth. A whale looks like a giant fish. But, did you know that whales are not fish? They are mammals. They have lungs to get air, just like people. Whales live in the ocean. The largest whale is the blue whale. A group of whales is called a herd.

Unscramble.

The _whale_ is the _largest_ animal on Earth.
l e w a h   g t a l e s r.
4 5 1 3 2   4 7 2 1 5 6 3

Circle.
What is a whale?   fish   (mammal)   turtle

Check.
What do whales and people have?   ☐ jackets
                                  ☑ lungs
                                  ☐ fins

Circle.
Where do whales live?
                      (ocean)   cave   river

Match.
group of whales ⤬ blue whale
largest whale ⤬ herd

Color the whale blue.

• Draw a herd of whales in the ocean.

Page 94

Learn About:
Polar Bears

Name_____

Polar bears live in a cold and snowy land. They are covered with thick, white fur. The fur helps keep them warm. Polar bears are tall and strong. They can be nine feet tall. They are good swimmers, too. They like to catch fish and seals. The white polar bear is hard to see on the white snow. How do you think this helps the polar bear?

Write.

Polar bears live in a _cold_ and _snowy_ land.
                    hot cold   snowy dry

Check.
☑ Polar bears are covered with thick, white fur.
☐ Polar bears are not good swimmers.
☑ Polar bears are tall and strong.

Circle.
What do polar bears like to catch?

fish   camel   seal

Put an X on the things that do not belong above.

• Draw a polar bear swimming in icy water.

Page 95

Learn About:
Penguins

Name_____

Do you think that all birds can fly? A penguin is a bird that cannot fly. Penguins stand on their back legs. Their walk looks like a waddle. Penguins have short, thick feathers. Their front is white. Their back is black. Penguins live mostly in cold oceans. They are very good swimmers.

Circle.
Yes or No
All birds can fly.   Yes (No)
A penguin is a bird that cannot fly.   (Yes) No
Penguins stand on their back legs.   (Yes) No
Penguins live mostly in cold oceans.   (Yes) No

Write.
A penguin's feathers are _short_ and _thick_
                        long short   thick thin

Write.
Penguins are good ☐ sailors.
                   ☑ swimmers.

Color.
Color the penguins: 1 - white   2 - black

• Draw three penguins swimming in a cold ocean.

Page 96

Answer Key

Learn About:

A Hippopotamus

Have you ever seen a hippopotamus at the zoo? A hippopotamus is the third largest land animal. Even a baby hippopotamus can be 100 pounds! A hippopotamus lives near a river, pond or lake. A hippopotamus is a good swimmer. It stays in the water much of the time.

Circle.

A hippopotamus is the (third) largest land animal.

Check.

A baby hippopotamus can be

☐ tiny and cute.
☑ 100 pounds.

Circle.

A hippopotamus likes to live near a:

(river)   town   (lake)   theater   (pond)

Unscramble.

A hippopotamus is a good _swimmer_
m i s w r m e
4 3 1 2 7 5 6

Color.

h - red
i - yellow
p - green
p - blue
o - purple

hippo

• Draw a baby hippopotamus in a river.

Page 97

Learn About:

A Seahorse

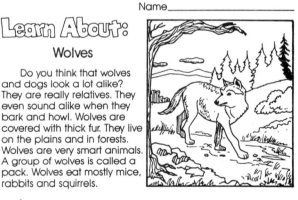

Do you know how the seahorse got its name? A seahorse is a small fish. Its head looks like a horse! The seahorse has a long tail. It wraps its tail around sea plants. It waits for tiny sea animals to come by. A seahorse has no teeth, so it sucks up the tiny animals for food. A seahorse cannot swim fast. Sometimes it hides in the plants from big fish.

Unscramble.

The _seahorse_ is a small ocean fish.
a r o h s s e e
3 6 5 4 1 7 2 8

Check.

How did the seahorse get its name?

☐ It eats hay like a horse.
☑ Its head looks like a horse.

Circle.

Yes or No

The seahorse has no teeth.   (Yes) No
The seahorse sucks up tiny animals.   (Yes) No
The seahorse has a saddle.   Yes (No)
The seahorse cannot swim fast.   (Yes) No

Color the seahorse brown.

• Draw a picture of a make-believe "seadog".

Page 98

Learn About:

Pelicans

A pelican is a large bird that lives near the water. A pelican has a large pouch under its bill. The pouch can hold water. A pelican also uses the pouch to catch fish. Pelicans can dive from the air into the water. They scoop up fish in their pouch. Pelicans are also strong fliers. Some pelicans can fly for hours without landing.

pouch   water   bird   bill   fish   dive   flier

Write.

1↓ I am a large b **i r d**.
2→ I live near the w **a t e r**.
3→ I have a large p **o u c h**.
4→ The pouch is under my b **i l l**.
5↓ I use the pouch to catch f **i s h**.
6→ I **d i v e** from the air into the water.
7↓ I am a strong f **l i e r**.

Write each answer in the puzzle above.

• Draw a pelican diving for fish.

Page 99

Learn About:

Wolves

Do you think that wolves and dogs look a lot alike? They are really relatives. They even sound alike when they bark and howl. Wolves are covered with thick fur. They live on the plains and in forests. Wolves are very smart animals. A group of wolves is called a pack. Wolves eat mostly mice, rabbits and squirrels.

Circle.

Yes or No

Wolves and dogs are relatives.   (Yes) No
Wolves and dogs bark and howl alike.   (Yes) No
Wolves are smaller than cats.   Yes (No)
Wolves are very smart animals.   (Yes) No

Check.

Where do most wolves live?

☑ plains
☐ ocean
☑ forests

Circle.

Wolves eat mostly:

(mice)   ducks   (rabbits)   (squirrels)

Color the wolf gray.

• Draw a pack of wolves.

Page 100

Answer Key

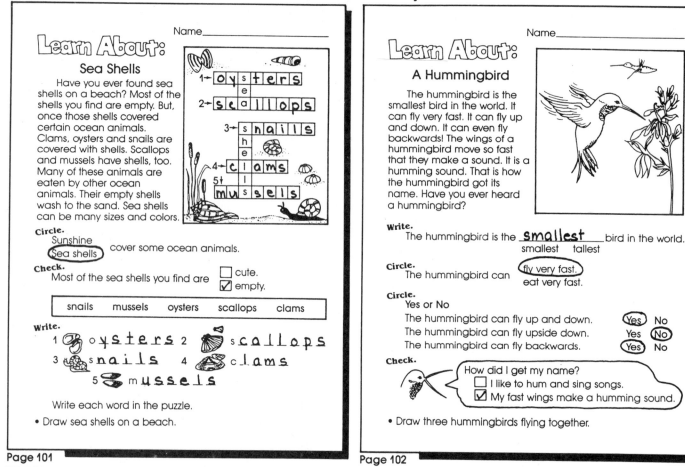

Page 101

Page 102

About the book . . .

Each book in this series capitalizes on the motivational value of commonly known student interests to enhance reading skills while expanding the learner's knowledge with a wealth of basic information.

The collections of informational readings with follow-up activities are designed to be effective tools for developing comprehension and vocabulary skills. These follow-up activities encompass such basic skills as sequencing, locating information, using the context, and following directions. Plus, an extended activity is provided with each reading to be used for enrichment or as a "challenge" for those who finish early.

About the author . . .

Holly Fitzgerald's special expertise in all areas of Language Arts has been gained by over fifteen years of varied teaching experiences at the elementary level. She also holds a Master's Degree in Education from Vanderbilt University.

Author: Holly Fitzgerald
Editor: Lee Quackenbush
Artist: Pat Biggs
Cover Art: Jan Vonk